THE HUBBLE ATLAS OF GALAXIES

ALLAN SANDAGE

Mount Wilson and Palomar Observatories, Carnegie Institution of Washington, California Institute of Technology

1961 · Publication 618

Carnegie Institution of Washington   WASHINGTON, D. C.

LIBRARY OF CONGRESS CATALOG CARD NUMBER 60–16568
Design and composition by The Stinehour Press
Plates and printing by The Meriden Gravure Company
Binding by Russell-Rutter Company
Line drawings by Felix Cooper and Frank Romano
Second Printing, 1962

Contents

Preface

IN 1953 Dr. Edwin Hubble was preparing an atlas of photographs to illustrate his revised classification system for galaxies. The motivation for his revision came from an inspection of photographs taken of all galaxies brighter than $m_{pg} = 13.0$ north of $\delta = -30°$ on the largest available scale. This magnificent set of plates was accumulated principally by Hubble from 1919 to 1948 with the Mount Wilson 60- and 100-inch telescopes. The revised system was completed by him between 1936 and 1950, but, unfortunately, the details of neither the revision of the classification nor the plans for the atlas were finished before his death in September 1953. Some notes and the fragments of a manuscript were found among his papers. They were sufficiently detailed to suggest the ideas that lay behind his new procedure, but there were only a few indications about which galaxies were to be considered prototypes of the various subclasses, or which ones were to be illustrated. When the decision was made to proceed with the atlas, it was clear that some additional work must precede the compilation and presentation of the material if justice was to be done to Hubble's insight and ideas.

It is impossible to know what combinations of facts Hubble had utilized to reach his conclusions. Many of his major points were equally difficult to understand because the notes were not detailed. However, implicit in the philosophy of science is the belief that any given scientific result can be reached by a number of diverse paths. In the particular case of this atlas, I inspected the same set of large-scale reflector plates that Hubble had used for his work. During this inspection, the notes and the conclusions of Hubble served as a guide to understanding what he had condensed and collated from the material. The reasons for his conclusions became clear as galaxy after galaxy was studied. The major groups, such as Sa, Sb, Sc, etc., were of course obvious, but the subgroups and the possible relations among them that his material suggested began to emerge and make sense. It should be emphasized that the major groupings and the suggested similarities which are discussed in the "Description of the Classification" are principally due to Hubble. I have acted mainly as an editor, not an editor of a manuscript but rather an editor of a set of ideas and conclusions that were implicit in the notes, in Hubble's grouping of galaxies into lists, in his notations on plate envelopes, in conversations with him from 1949 to 1953, and in the scheme as it emerged from inspection of the same material that he had used to define his system.

The detailed descriptions of the classes in the descriptive section are of mixed origin. Preliminary drafts of the sections on E, S0, Sa, and SB0 galaxies were found in Hubble's papers. These formed the skeleton of the present discussion. However, changes were made in part of the notation, in the descriptions of the individual galaxies (based on recent data obtained with the 200-inch), and in the relations of the subgroups.

There is hope that this atlas is close to what Hubble himself had planned to publish. The format, the choice of galaxies to illustrate, the descriptions of these galaxies, and the division and notation of the subgroups were not specified by Hubble, but the present atlas may be an approximation to his original design for an illustrated volume.

The work of making the photographic reproductions from the original negatives was done in the laboratory at the Mount Wilson offices by Stuart Bowen under the direction of William C. Miller, the staff photographer. The excellence of the reproductions is due in large part to the skill of these two men. Their willingness to experiment and their patience with the whims of the compiler made this part of the work easy.

It is a particular pleasure to thank Robert E. Sears, chief night assistant on the 200-inch telescope, for his aid in obtaining many of the plates used in this atlas. He worked not only with me but with every other observer whose plates appear in this book. Observing at a telescope, even under the best conditions, is tedious. Under the worst, it can be cold and miserable. Sears was a great help.

ALLAN SANDAGE

Mount Wilson and Palomar Observatories
Pasadena, California
April, 1959

Galaxies

WHAT are galaxies? No one knew before 1900. Very few people knew in 1920. All astronomers knew after 1924.

Galaxies are the largest single aggregates of stars in the universe. They are to astronomy what atoms are to physics. Each galaxy is a stellar system somewhat like our Milky Way, and isolated from its neighbors by nearly empty space. In popular terms, each galaxy is a separate "island universe" unto itself. The average density of matter in a galaxy is only 10^{-23} gram for every cubic centimeter. If this matter were spread over all of space in a uniform way, a density of only 10^{-30} to 10^{-31} g/cm³ would result. Less than one-millionth of the total volume of the universe is occupied by condensations of matter.

It is almost certain that individual galaxies have not always been what they are today. We see the universe some 10 billion years after its last creation, but clues to its initial conditions remain. There has not been sufficient time for them to be obliterated, and if the proper observations are made and are properly interpreted, we can hope to reconstruct a history of its evolution. This hope drives cosmologists to think, causes large telescopes to be built, and makes observers work on cold winter nights. The hope is not vain. We do stand a chance of understanding the universe. And the present generation, with its great telescopes and its physical theories, may catch glimpses of the early stages of time.

A renaissance is occurring today in astronomy. It began in the 1920's, when physicists and theoretical astronomers asked, "What are the stars?" The theory of the stellar interior was developed by Eddington, his predecessors, his contemporaries, and his followers. The essence of the theory was published in one of the most important books ever written, Eddington's *Internal Constitution of the Stars*. This work opened the way for modern theories of stellar evolution—a field that is now in its infancy but which promises to consolidate many of the isolated facts in astronomy.

The theory of stellar structure combines the small-scale phenomena of the atoms with the intermediate-scale phenomena of the stars. But during the 1920's science was also advancing in cosmology, which has as its scope the largest-scale phenomena possible to observe—those of the universe itself. We are now at the crossroads. Insights deriving from the theory of stellar evolution are being applied to cosmological data from the universe at large. Out of the combination we now have a reasonable account of the formation of the elements, the beginnings of a theory for the evolution of galaxies themselves, and explanations for the presence or absence of all components of the stellar contents of galaxies. There is an exciting time ahead, limited only by the size of the telescopes and the ingenuity of the workers. This first chapter of the Hubble Atlas sketches cosmological thinking in the field of galaxies and the major change in it that took place in 1920. Some of the problems that lie in the immediate future for which there is good hope of a solution are then suggested.

Faint, nebulous objects with a discernible surface area have been known in the sky since the invention of the telescope. Speculation as to their nature was not confined to astronomers, but such men as Immanuel Kant (1724–1804), Emanuel Swedenborg (1688–1772), and Thomas Wright (1711–1786) entered the field. These three men introduced and discussed on purely philosophical grounds the island-universe hypothesis, which held that the small white nebulae scattered over the sky were systems of stars at such great distances that the individual stellar contents could not be distinguished. Owing to the lack of observational data, the idea did not flourish but remained one of the many unproved scientific speculations so characteristic of the period.

Although the nature of the nebulae was not understood until much later, catalogues of the objects were made by many of the prominent observers of the eighteenth and nineteenth centuries. The first major discovery survey was that of Sir William Herschel (1738–1822), who, by visual methods, systematically observed the northern sky from England with telescopes of his own design and manufacture.

Herschel, a professional musician in his early years and later the first president of the Royal Astronomical Society and the private astronomer to King George III, was one of the most influential and industrious observers of all time. His catalogue of nebulae and star clusters was begun in the 1780's. A copy of a preliminary catalogue of 1000 nebulae and clusters was presented to the Royal Society in 1786; it was followed in 1789 by a second edition containing 1000 additional entries, and in 1802 by a third list of 500 nebulae.

Herschel's only son, John, continued the work of his father by taking the telescopes to Capetown, South Africa. The General Catalogue of Nebulae was published by Sir John Herschel in the *Philosophical Transactions* of 1864. It contains 5079 objects, of which 4630 were discovered by the two Herschels and 449 by others. This catalogue is of great historical interest, but it is not used today because a far more comprehensive and complete one was published by J. L. E. Dreyer in 1888.

Dreyer's compilation is called *A New General Catalogue of Nebulae and Clusters of Stars*. This catalogue and the two supplements issued in 1895 and 1908, and called the first and second Index Catalogues, are extensively used today. They are published in the *Memoirs of the Royal Astronomical Society*, volumes 49, 51, and 59. The galaxies discussed in the present atlas are identified by their NGC or IC numbers.

The field days of the cataloguers were over by 1908. Positions and descriptions of nearly 15,000 nebulae and star clusters were known, but the true nature of the nebulae was still a mystery. The solution of the problem belonged to the era of great telescopes and photographic plates which began in 1908 with the construction of the 60-inch reflector on Mount Wilson, and continued with the completion of the 100-inch telescope on the same mountain. These instruments, each the largest in the world when it was built, gave the necessary data. The question ultimately reduced to the problem of distances to the nebulae. If these distances were small compared with the size of our own galaxy, the white nebulae were members of our galaxy. If the distances were very large, the nebulae were probably systems of stars in their own right. Hubble summarized the problem in his book *The Realm of the Nebulae* in the following way:

> The status of the nebulae . . . was undetermined because the distances were wholly unknown. They were definitely beyond the limits of direct measurement, and the scanty, indirect evidence bearing on the problem could be interpreted in various ways. The nebulae might be relatively nearby objects and hence members of the stellar system, or they might be very remote and hence inhabitants of outer space. At this point, the development of nebular research came into immediate contact with the philosophical theory of island universes. The theory represented, in principle, one of the alternative solutions of the problem of nebular distances. The question of distances was frequently put in the form: Are nebulae island universes?

The solution came unexpectedly and dramatically. The chain of events began in 1917 with the chance discovery of a nova in NGC 6946 by Ritchey with the 60-inch telescope (*Harvard Bulletin* 641, July 28, 1917). This particular nova was not important in itself. It reached only 14.6 apparent magnitude. But the discovery caused Ritchey to look back through the entire plate collection of the Mount Wilson Observatory to see whether similar events had occurred in other nebulae. The search netted two novae which occurred on plates of the Andromeda Nebula (M31) taken with the 60-inch in 1909. The announcement of Ritchey's discovery in NGC 6946 stimulated H. D. Curtis, then at the Lick Observatory, to inspect old plates taken with the Crossley 36-inch reflector. Curtis discovered a nova in NGC 4227 and two in NGC

2

4321, and reported the discoveries in *Harvard Bulletin* 642. All three of the stars were undoubtedly supernovae in the modern notation, but this separation into normal and supernovae was not made until much later.

Curtis discussed the six novae known in 1917 for their connection with the island-universe hypothesis, and, cautiously, stated his belief that these novae favored the extragalactic nature of the white nebulae. The two jokers in this deck of six novae were S Andromedae and Z Centauri. S Andromedae appeared near the center of the Andromeda Nebula (M31) in 1885 and reached 7.2 visual magnitude. Z Centauri was discovered near the center of NGC 5253 in July 1895, when it was about 7th magnitude. Both these novae were abnormally bright and gave discordant values for the distances. However, two months after the announcement of Ritchey's discovery of the nova in NGC 6946, various workers had assembled a list of eleven novae in seven different nebulae, four of them in M31.

Shapley discussed the implication of the data (*Publications of the Astronomical Society of the Pacific*, *29*, 213, 1917) for the island-universe hypothesis, and concluded, as did Curtis, that, if the novae in spirals were comparable with the twenty-six known at that time in our own galaxy, M31 must be about a million light years distant—which made the nebulae external galaxies. Curtis believed this conclusion; Shapley did not. Shapley argued that the data were conflicting because of two points: (1) S Andromedae would have to be much brighter than other novae found in M31, and (2) van Maanen's measurements of the proper motions of the spiral arms of nebulae showed large values. Van Maanen's angular displacements, combined with a great distance demanded by the island-universe theory, gave velocities in spiral arms close to or greater than the velocity of light! And so the debate began. And the history of this debate is at once fascinating and sobering to any student of science.

The two principal figures in the controversy between 1917 and 1921 in the United States were H. D. Curtis and Harlow Shapley. Both men strongly believed their own position. Belief is never an entirely rational thing. It comes partly from a logical sifting of all facts, but also from intuition and deep philosophical yearnings for a system of ideas. Everyone, once his belief is set,

will rationalize the facts to suit himself. The debate in question is an excellent example of the process. We, in 1960, have an almost unique test case here. The arguments, pro and con, as they were advanced in 1917 to 1921, constitute a psychological study of the first order. Perhaps the fairest statement that can be made is that Shapley used many of the correct arguments but came to the wrong conclusion. Curtis, whose intuition was better in this case, gave rather weak and sometimes incorrect arguments from the facts, but reached the correct conclusion. The most powerful statements by these astronomers were published in the *Pubs. A. S. P.*, *31*, 261, 1919, by Shapley in a paper entitled "On the Existence of External Galaxies," and in the *Journal of the Washington Academy of Sciences*, *9*, 217, 1919, by Curtis in a paper called "Modern Theories of Spiral Nebulae." Every student of the subject should read these two papers.

A third man entered the debate in 1919: Knut Lundmark, in Sweden. In the interval between 1917 and 1919, twenty-two novae had been discovered in M31. They were analyzed by Lundmark in his doctor's thesis in 1920. Lundmark made the assumption that novae in M31 were objects comparable to novae in our own stellar system, and, with his preliminary absolute magnitude calibration of $M_{pg} = -4$ at maximum, arrived at a distance to M31 of 650,000 light years. Lundmark neglected S Andromedae in this computation and assumed that two classes of novae existed—an "upper class," now identified as supernovae, and a "lower class," now identified as normal novae. Because of the discrepant case of S Andromedae, which at Lundmark's distance to M31 would have an absolute magnitude of $M_{pg} = -16.0$, the problem was not definitely solved in the minds of most astronomers. Furthermore, van Maanen's proper motions of the knots in spiral arms of seven nebulae seemed to put an absolute quietus on the island-universe hypothesis. An impasse had clearly been reached.

But both sides continued to marshal their arguments. Lundmark, during a visit to the Lick Observatory in 1921, began a study of the near-by Sc galaxy M33. He obtained a number of slitless spectra of its spiral arms. The brightest resolved stars in the arms showed normal spectra. Lundmark commented

3

in a paper in *Pubs. A. S. P.*, *33*, 324, 1921, "Some objects [in the arms] have a nebular spectrum but most of the objects belonging to the spiral show a strong continuous spectrum without bright lines. It is of course hard to give the accurate spectral type but a solar or somewhat earlier type seems to be predominant. From the spectral evidence it seems probable that the spiral nebula consists of ordinary stars, clusters of stars, and some nebular [i.e., gaseous] material"; and later, in the same paper, "If we attribute to the brightest resolved stars in the spiral arms [of M33] an absolute magnitude of -6^m we get a parallax for the nebula of: $\pi = 0\rlap{.}''000003$." This corresponds to a distance of 1,000,000 light years, which is very close to the modern value.

One other doubt clouded the issue in these early years. The 60-inch telescope had been used on many occasions by Ritchey and Pease to photograph the outer regions of M31 and M33. These galaxies are so near (they are members of the Local Group) that the separate stars in the spiral arms are easily resolved (see for example the 100-inch negative print of M33 in the *Astrophysical Journal*, *127*, 513, 1958). But the early observers did not describe the photographs as if resolution into stars had occurred; rather, they called the resolved objects "nebulous stars" with images "softer" than those of normal stars. Most astronomers therefore believed that stars had not been detected in M31 and M33. Arguments comparing the apparent magnitudes of such nebulous images with stars in our own galaxy were not taken seriously. The opinion of the opposition about the resolution of M33 into stars was stated by Shapley in 1919 in *Pubs. A. S. P.*, *31*, 265, 1919:

> With one or two possible exceptions the secondary nuclei in spiral nebulae are so distinctly nebulous that they cannot be considered individual stars. Even in Messier 33, probably the most conspicuously nucleated of the brighter spirals, it is easy on large-scale plates to distinguish between the superposed stellar images and the "softer" nebular condensations. It is possible, however, to see a resemblance of these diffuse nebulous objects to extremely distant stellar clusters, but unless we introduce further unverified assumptions the analogy breaks down when the observed colors are intercompared.

The culmination of the argument was reached in the famous Shapley-Curtis debate held before the National Academy of Sciences on April 26, 1920. Two

papers were published in the *Bulletin of the National Research Council*, volume 2, part 3, May 1921. The concluding paragraphs of each paper illustrate the situation. Shapley stated:

> It seems to me that the evidence, other than the admittedly critical tests depending on the size of the galaxy, is opposed to the view that the spirals are galaxies of stars comparable with our own. In fact, there appears as yet no reason for modifying the tentative hypothesis that the spirals are not composed of typical stars at all, but are truly nebulous objects. Three very recent results are, I believe, distinctly serious for the theory that spiral nebulae are comparable galaxies—(1) Seares' deduction that none of the known spiral nebulae has a surface brightness as small as that of our galaxy; (2) Reynolds' study of the distribution of light and color in typical spirals, from which he concludes they cannot be stellar systems; and (3) van Maanen's recent measures of rotation in the spiral M33, corroborating his earlier work on Messier 101 and 81, and indicating that these bright spirals cannot reasonably be the excessively distant objects required by the theory.

Curtis's concluding arguments are not summarized in a single paragraph, and so his points cannot be quoted in detail. His final paragraph is:

> I hold, therefore, to the belief that the galaxy is probably not more than 30,000 light-years in diameter; that the spirals are not intra-galactic objects but island universes, like our own galaxy, and that the spirals, as external galaxies, indicate to us a greater universe into which we may penetrate to distances of ten million to a hundred million light-years.

Clearly neither side had convinced the other. New data were needed to place the solution beyond all doubt. Edwin Hubble provided these crucial data by his discovery, analysis, and interpretation of cepheid variable stars in M31, M33, and NGC 6822. This discovery settled the controversy once and for all. It proved beyond question that nebulae were external galaxies of dimensions comparable to our own. It opened the last frontier of astronomy, and gave, for the first time, the correct conceptual view of the universe. Galaxies are the units of matter that define the granular structure of the universe itself.

The announcement of Hubble's discovery was dramatic. It occurred at the thirty-third meeting of the American Astronomical Society, held in Washington, D. C., from December 30, 1924, to January 1, 1925. Hubble was not present but sent his paper to be read. Joel Stebbins, many years later, reminisced on this meeting and recalled that, when Hubble's paper had been read, the entire Society knew that the debate had come to an end, that the island-universe concept of the distribution of matter in space had been proved, and that an era of enlightenment in cosmology had begun. Both Shapley and Curtis were present at the meeting. Perhaps they exchanged comments over a drink and a cigar.

An abstract of Hubble's paper was published in the *Publications of the American Astronomical Society, 5*, 261, 1925. It was reprinted in the *Observatory, 48*, 139, 1925. Hubble followed his announcement by three exhaustive papers on the stellar contents of M31, M33, and NGC 6822, in which data on the cepheids were presented, together with discussions of novae and the brightest resolved stars. These papers appear in the *Astrophysical Journal, 62*, 409, 1925; *63*, 236, 1926; and *69*, 103, 1929.

The way was now open for an earnest attack on the cosmological problem, for it was clear for the first time that a fair sample of the universe was available for study with large telescopes.

The master problem in cosmology is to understand the distribution and motions of galaxies as they relate to the origin and evolution of the universe. Two distinct approaches are possible and necessary.

First, the stellar content of galaxies must be described, classified, and studied. The classification should relate class properties of the objects by finding a continuous sequence of forms. This is possible if the galaxies have really evolved and if both the old and the new forms exist at the present time. The problem is analogous to proving biological evolution by reading the fossil record and classifying the bones in a continuous sequence.

The second approach is a study of the way galaxies, as systems, define the large-scale distribution and motion of matter in the universe. Hubble pioneered in both these approaches. (With regard to the second approach, it suffices to say that its elucidation led to the discovery of the expansion of the universe, with all the consequences for geometry and relativity. A discussion of this phase of Hubble's work is out of place in this atlas, because we are concerned here only with the geometrical forms of the galaxies themselves.)

A system for the classification of galaxies was presented by Hubble to the I. A. U. in 1925 and was later published in the *Astrophysical Journal, 64*, 321, 1926. This system, or a slight variation of it, has been universally adopted. The present atlas describes Hubble's last revision and illustrates the complete sequence of classification from the E galaxies through the true spirals to the irregulars. Hubble was careful, in all his writings on the classification problem, to avoid an evolutionary connotation to the sequence of forms. He did introduce the terms "early" and "late" galaxies as a convenience of terminology, but he specifically pointed out that these temporal words did not signify to him a direction of evolution, or even that evolution of a given galaxy through the sequence ever occurs. This attitude is maintained in the present atlas, at least in the presentation of the classification. However, facts deriving from the stellar content of galaxies of different types (Sa, Sb, Sc, etc.), combined with the theory of evolution of individual stars that has developed in recent years, make it clear that the problem of the evolution of galaxies *can* be approached today on other than speculative terms.

Study of the illustrations in this atlas immediately reveals one fact. There is an almost one-to-one correspondence between the presence of dust and the presence of bright, blue O and B stars. Such stars are known to be very young because their nuclear energy sources can last for only a few million years. Since they are visible today, they must have been created within the last several million years. It is invariably the Irr, Sc, and SBc galaxies that contain these young stars. Sb and SBb galaxies have bright resolved stars, but they are fainter than those in the Irr, Sc, and SBc systems. The presence of dust and highly resolved spiral arms goes hand in hand with other characteristics of the spiral arms. Whenever the arm system is tightly wound, as in Sa and early Sb galaxies, there is little or no resolution of the arms into stars, and there is very little dust. Star formation is not going on in these galaxies now; the dust has been used up; and the arms, which were loosely wound and highly branched in the Sc stage, have wound themselves tight against the periphery of the lens by the shearing and stretching action of the differential velocity field. A hint of this process is discussed in the Sb section in the next chapter and also in the legends to the illustrations, especially in the description of NGC 5055.

The Hubble Atlas

The Sa, SBa, S0, SB0, and E galaxies show little or no resolution into bright stars or H II regions. Star formation has apparently stopped completely, because all the necessary dust has been used up. These galaxies contain stars that are very old and are in a state of evolution characterized by such star clusters as M3 and M67 in our own galaxy. Baade's study of the stellar content of the central regions of M31 and the outer regions of NGC 205 and M32 proves this point. No new stars are being formed here; there is no dust; and the stars that are resolved (see page 2 of the illustrations) are red giants at the top of a globular-cluster-like color-magnitude diagram.

The present view, which is only hinted at here and which must be worked out in detail with the facts marshaled, suggests that a given galaxy begins as an Irr or Sc (SBc). There is much dust and gas available for star formation. Each successive generation of star formation uses up the raw material (dust and gas) until little of that material is left. The differential velocity field in each galaxy (plus perhaps magnetic fields) controls the nature of the spiral arms. When star formation ceases, the arms tighten up (as in NGC 488) and the galaxy evolves into an Sb type. The bright stars die, and are therefore not present to form the lumpy condensations in the arms. They are not replaced by new stars, for the formation of stars has ceased. The faint stars that remain are red and are *not* distributed in spiral arms because random motions have wiped away the separate arm structures. At this stage, the galaxy is an Sa system. When all arms are gone, and no stars are being formed, the system becomes an S0.

This is not the place to present in detail the evidence for these ideas. The point here is that, before any theory of evolution has a chance of being correct, a classification of galaxies must be made, and the "fossil record," as it were, examined. This indeed was Hubble's basic motivation for his classification scheme, and it is the justification for this book.

The present classification was devised by Hubble before evolutionary hypotheses were ever attempted. So, today, the belief that evolution proceeds from the Sc through the Sb and Sa groups to the S0 does not negate the form in which the classification sequence is given from E through S0 to Sa, Sb, Sc,

and Irr. The continuity of the sequence is still present; only the direction of travel is reversed. The words "early" and "late" are used in this atlas in the classical sense introduced by Hubble; i.e., Sc galaxies are "later" in the classification than Sb's.

At this point it is well to quote directly from Hubble about the purpose of the classification. The following paragraphs were probably written in 1936 for the dedication of the McDonald Observatory:

> The ultimate problems in the field of nebular research may be stated in the following terms. First is the representation of the observed structure and of the dynamics of nebulae as particular stages in the evolutionary history of stellar systems; second is the problem of inferring the nature of the universe from the observed characteristics of the sample available for inspection. Results obtained during the past years permit the problems to be formulated with some confidence, but the solutions are still in the future.
>
> The significant evidence is accumulating unevenly along the various lines of approach. As regards the problem of the structure and dynamics of the nebulae, the two elements are in quite different stages of development. On the one hand, current discussions of dynamics are largely hypothetical because they depend upon internal motions (observed as radial velocities), and such data are almost wholly lacking. For instance, the direction of rotation with respect to the spiral pattern is not generally agreed upon by all astronomers, nor is it known whether the points of ejection of the arms rotate with the nebulae or remain fixed in space. Until these essential questions are settled by sound observational evidence, the discussion of the origin and development of spiral arms will remain speculative. On the other hand, the structural forms of nebulae can be investigated with confidence because the necessary data are already available in the collections of direct photographs made with large reflectors.

It is this latter problem of the structural forms to which the present atlas is directed. This *Hubble Atlas* is but one stage in a developing program of nebular research. The field was opened primarily by Hubble. He carried research along multiple channels of the cosmological problem only to be stopped before the final answers could be found. His followers owe a debt to this pioneer cosmologist. Paraphrasing one of Hubble's own comments: The solution of the cosmological problem is an achievement reserved for great telescopes. As telescopes and techniques improve, astronomers eventually reach a critical barrier of ignorance. In due course this barrier falls. The breach, when open, permits all to follow.

Description of the Classification

THE most widely used classification system for galaxies is that proposed by Hubble in 1925 (*Transactions of the I. A. U.*, *2*, 1925, Commission 28; *Astrophysical Journal*, *64*, 321, 1926). A slightly revised version of this first system was later described by him in his book *The Realm of the Nebulae* (Yale University Press, 1936, chapter II). A review of the system of 1936, prepared by Hubble as an introduction to this atlas, was found in a manuscript fragment among his papers. It is likely that this review was written between 1947 and 1950. A part of the manuscript reads:

> The sequence of classification, as originally presented, consisted of a series of elliptical nebulae ranging from globular (E0) to lenticular (E7) forms, and two parallel series of unwinding spirals, normal (S) and barred (SB). Each of the latter series was subdivided into three sections, termed early, intermediate, and late, and designated by the letters a, b, and c, respectively. Thus the early, normal spirals were represented by the symbol Sa, and the early barred spirals by SBa.
>
> The data available in 1936 seemed to indicate a smooth and continuous transition from elliptical nebulae to barred spirals, and, in fact, the first section of the latter series, SBa, exhibited no spiral arms. The corresponding section of the normal series, Sa, contained so many nebulae with fully developed spiral arms that, where arms could not be definitely recognized, their presence was assumed, and the failure to detect them was attributed to effects of orientation or other causes. The procedure was unsatisfactory because it introduced subdivisions in the parallel series of spirals that were clearly out of step. Moreover, the transition from E7 to Sa appeared so abrupt that, if real, it might be regarded as cataclysmic.
>
> With accumulating data, and especially with the increasing number of good photographs with the 100-inch reflector, the situation has clarified. Numerous systems are now recognized which are later than E7 but which show neither bars nor spiral structure. These nebulae fill the supposed gap between E7 and Sa and remove the excuse for postulating a cataclysmic transition. [These transition galaxies are designated S0. They are actually found in nature and are no longer a hypothetical class, as was once believed; see *The Realm of the Nebulae*, pages 45–46, and the legend to figure 1, page 45, of the Yale University Press edition of 1936. A. S.]
>
> A similar group of objects corresponds to the section [called SBa in the 1936 classification]. This situation emphasizes the desirability of redefining the sections of both series in a more comparable manner.

Hubble then goes on to explain the major difference between the classification system of 1936 and the new system described here for the first time.

> The revision might be made in various ways but only that actually adopted will be described. First, two new types, S0 and SB0, have been introduced to include objects later than E7 but with no trace of spiral structure. Secondly, the series of true spirals, as before, are subdivided into the three sections Sa, Sb, Sc, and SBa, SBb, SBc. In the case of the normal spirals, the change amounts to a subdivision of the former section Sa into the two sections S0 and Sa. In the case of the barred spirals the entire former section, SBa, is now termed SB0, and the former section SBb is subdivided into the two sections SBa and SBb. The revisions are summarized in the following table:

Old Class	New Class	Old Class	New Class
Sa	⎰ S0 ⎱ Sa	SBa	SB0
Sb	Sb	SBb	⎰ SBa ⎱ SBb
Sc	Sc	SBc	SBc

> The introduction of the new types leads to a revision of the original assignment of symbols. The original SBa nebulae are now described as SB0, and the original SBb nebulae are redistributed between SBa and SBb. Among the normal spirals, the Sa objects are redistributed between S0 and Sa. Otherwise the system remains unchanged.
>
> The transition stages, S0 and SB0, are firmly established. In both sequences, the nebulae may be described as systems definitely later than E7 but showing no spiral structure. The next stages, Sa and SBa, are represented by nebulae which

show incipient spiral structure. Fully developed spirals are distributed over the two later stages of each sequence according to the relative extent of the unresolved central region, and the degree to which the arms are resolved and unwound.

With this general description as introduction, we turn to the details of the classification. The classification criteria together with the prototype examples are presented in the following pages. Most of the galaxies mentioned here are illustrated in this atlas, and more detailed descriptions of the galaxies are given in the legends facing the illustrations. These descriptions show how the type examples fit into the developing classification sequence.

ELLIPTICAL GALAXIES

THE images of elliptical galaxies have complete rotational symmetry. The galaxies themselves are undoubtedly figures of revolution with two equal principal axes. The third, the axis of rotation, is smaller than the other two.

Subclassification into ellipticity groups is made from the geometry of the projected image. The individual true ellipticities of the meridian sections are unknown except in the pure class E7 because the orientation of the principal axes to the line of sight is never known. The apparent ellipticities are expressed as $10(a-b)/a$, where a and b are the diameters of the major and minor axes, respectively. The observed classes range from E0 to E7. No elliptical galaxies are known that are flatter than E7. Galaxies whose central sections *are* flatter invariably show an outer region of low surface brightness which resembles a thin, fundamental plane. Such galaxies are classed as $S0_1$ and are shown on page *4* of the illustrations.

8

The surface brightness of true E galaxies decreases smoothly from the nucleus, closely following the equation $I=I_0(r/a + 1)^{-2}$. Here r is the nuclear distance, and a is a parameter which differs from galaxy to galaxy. The photographic images appear completely smooth with no breaks or inflections in the luminosity gradient. There are no traces of resolution into stars, knots, or H II regions in E galaxies beyond the Local Group. The E galaxies within the Local Group, however, have been resolved into myriads of faint stars by Baade with the 100- and the 200-inch telescopes. This was a major achievement, giving, for the first time, definite knowledge of the stellar content of these systems.

The absolute visual magnitude of the brightest stars in E galaxies is about $M_V=-3.0$. The stars are red with international color indices of about 1.5. They are probably in the same stage of their evolutionary history as stars in globular clusters. E galaxies have no bright blue stars like those in the spiral arms of Sb, Sc, Irr, SBb, and SBc systems. There is also no optical evidence for dust. Perhaps the most significant observational fact deriving from the classification of galaxies is the almost one-to-one relation between the presence of dust and the presence of young blue O and B supergiant stars of $M_V \approx -9$. The converse also holds. Where there is no dust there are no young stars. We are forced to two conclusions: (1) young stars are formed from dust; (2) E galaxies either never had dust or they transformed their dust into stars at an early epoch and are now incapable of forming new stars. The absence of spiral arms in E galaxies suggests a third conclusion: (3) the presence of dust is essential for the formation of spiral structure. This third conclusion is not so simple, however, because many galaxies illustrated in this atlas have chaotic dust patterns but no spiral structure. Examples are NGC 4753 (page *8*), M82 (page *41*), and NGC 3077 (page *41*). Consequently, other conditions besides the presence of dust are prerequisites for the creation and maintenance of a spiral pattern. In any event, E galaxies represent an important stage in any theory of galaxies because conditions appear to be rather simple in them. The stars are old. They are in an evolutionary state which is fairly well understood. No new stars are being formed. There is no dust. There are no spiral arms. E galaxies do, however, have gas at very low densities. The evidence is the presence of emission lines in the spectra due to forbidden [O II] at λ3727, and Hα which is probably present whenever 3727 occurs. Most E galaxies show this emission.

It should be emphasized that the ellipticities of the images of E galaxies are apparent ellipticities only. They result from the projection of the true spheroid on the plane of the sky. A true E5, for example, can appear in projection as anything from E0 to E5, depending on the orientation of the symmetry axis to the line of sight. Because of this effect, many more apparent E0 galaxies exist in projection than in space. The effect of projection can be allowed for statistically if it is assumed that the symmetry axes are orientated at random in space (Hubble, *Astrophysical Journal*, *64*, 321, 1926; M. A. Machiels, *Bulletin astronomique*, Mémoires et variétés, VI, 322, 1930). A computation shows that the true ellipticities of E galaxies are distributed nearly uniformly from E0 to E7 in the true classes.

The isophotal contours of the projected images of E galaxies are similar ellipses (Hubble, *Astrophysical Journal*, *71*, 231, 1930) except those of E7 systems, where the ends of the major axes are drawn into sharp points (Oort, *Astrophysical Journal*, *91*, 273, 1940). It may be possible to discover the orientation of the rotation axis to the line of sight by precise photometry to determine differences in the isophotal contours between galaxies of different true types but with the same apparent type. But such differences are known to be very small, and they will be difficult to detect.

Eleven E galaxies, ranging from E0 to E7, are illustrated in this atlas. The points to note are (1) the smooth texture of the photographic image, (2) the smooth gradient of surface brightness from the nucleus outward, (3) the absence of dust, and (4) the lack of any suggestion of resolution into bright blue stars or knots (compare with any Sb or Sc galaxy, such as NGC 5055 or NGC 4699). Some of the systems illustrated on pages *1*, *2*, and *3* of the atlas show condensations across the face of the photographic image. This is particularly true of NGC 4486 (M87), NGC 4636, and NGC 4278. These condensations are very likely globular clusters associated with the galaxy in question. The brightest of the condensations have the correct absolute magnitude ($M_{pg} \approx -10$), and there is every other reason to expect globular clusters to be associated with E galaxies. They are definitely known to occur in M32, NGC 205, NGC 185, NGC 147, and the Fornax system, all of which are E galaxies in the Local Group.

NGC 3115 was originally classified as E7 by Hubble. Plates taken with the 200-inch, however, showed the presence of sharp points at both ends of the major axis. These points had previously been found by Hubble and by Oort in their photometry of 3115. The illustration of this galaxy on page *1* of the atlas shows the feature. The points suggest the beginning of a fundamental plane similar to that found in $S0_1$ systems (see the description of $S0_1$ in the next section). Consequently, NGC 3115 is no longer considered a pure E7 but rather a "transition" between E7 and $S0_1$.

NGC 4486, besides having an abnormal number of globular clusters, possesses a unique feature in its central regions, namely, a jet of luminous matter starting in the nucleus. A short-exposure plate of this jet is shown on page *2* of the atlas. The spectrum is known to be continuous, with no emission or absorption lines (Humason, quoted by Baade and Minkowski, *Astrophysical Journal*, *119*, 222, 1954). The knots in the jet were discovered to be polarized (Baade, *Astrophysical Journal*, *123*, 550, 1956). Other reproductions of NGC 4486 and its jet are given by Baade and Minkowski in the references just quoted.

The resolution of E galaxies into stars is illustrated on page *3* of the atlas. NGC 205, NGC 185, and Leo II are shown. All are members of the Local Group. Close inspection of the illustration of NGC 185 and 205 shows that the brightest resolved stars are of the same brightness. This fact explains the observation that resolution does not occur until a critical exposure time is reached, at which time the entire smooth image of the galaxy breaks up into individual stars. This phenomenon is described in two papers by Baade in the *Astrophysical Journal*, *100*, 137 and 147, 1944.

NGC 205 and 185 are classed as E peculiar because the luminosity gradient, seen on plates inspected by eye, appears to be less steep than that of M32 and most other E systems; i.e., the two peculiar galaxies are less compact. This description is subjective, however. The $I(r)$ curves probably follow the normal inverse-square relation found to hold for other E galaxies. There are a few dust patches across the face of NGC 205, which do not show well in the illustration. As might be expected, a few bright blue supergiants are associated with this dust. (See the reproduction of the nuclear regions of NGC 205 from a plate taken in ultraviolet light by Baade, *Observatory of the University of Michigan Publications*, no. X, 1950.)

The final E galaxy illustrated is Leo II. This is representative of the class of dwarf ellipticals of low absolute magnitude and extremely low surface brightness. The class includes the Sculptor and Fornax systems (Baade and Hubble, *Publications of the Astronomical Society of the Pacific*, *51*, 40, 1938), the Draco system, Ursa Minor system, Leo I, and Leo II (A. G. Wilson, *Pubs. A. S. P.*, *67*, 27, 1955). Note the lack of compactness, and the extreme resolvability into stars. The color-magnitude diagram for the Draco system is similar to that of globular clusters.

S0 GALAXIES

THE S0 class was not recognized in Hubble's first paper on classification in 1926. As more and more large-scale reflector plates were accumulated between 1926 and 1936, the preliminary classification system was modified and refined. Hubble came to believe that a transition type was required to bridge the gap between the ellipticals and the spirals. In Hubble's 1936 description of his classification (see chapter II of *The Realm of the Nebulae*), a hypothetical transition class S0 was introduced, which had not been established observationally. Between 1936 and 1950, however, the photographic survey of the near-by galaxies was completed, and the S0 class was established empirically. Its features have never been discussed in the literature. The class is defined by the examples shown in the atlas and is described here for the first time.

S0 galaxies have symmetrical forms which are flatter than E7 but which show no spiral structure and no trace of bars. The characteristic features are a bright nucleus, a central lens surrounded by a faint and sometimes extensive envelope, and, in the later stages of the section, circular absorption lanes.

S0 galaxies appear to form a transition between the E galaxies and the true spirals. It is well established observationally that no elliptical galaxies exist whose fundamental planes have a larger flattening ratio than 1 to 3, whereas all spiral galaxies have fundamental planes whose flattening ratios *are* larger than 1 to 3. These results suggest that there exists a critical eccentricity of the central section of E systems. Some type of dynamical instability seems to begin in galaxies whose eccentricity is greater than this critical value. Galaxies that have angular momenta greater than the critical value tend to take up forms whose central sections are more eccentric than E7, and, for these, the instability causes matter to slough off the central regions and to spread out into a thin, disk-shaped structure which constitutes the fundamental plane. The resulting equilibrium form then consists of a dense nuclear region embedded in a thin disk or envelope. This may not, of course, be a correct description of the formation of the S0 forms, but the observed features of the class can be accounted for in this way. At any rate, the S0 appear to be important in any scheme of classification. They have the highly flattened fundamental plane of the true spirals together with the amorphous texture and the absence of dust and spiral arms of the E galaxies. It is of interest that the luminosity distribution of S0 galaxies could be obtained by removing the bright resolved stars, the dust, and the spiral structure of spiral galaxies. That is to say, the luminosity distribution of the "type II" stars in M31, for example, resembles the distribution of S0 galaxies.

The transition from E to S0 is smooth and continuous. The gradual merging of the classes introduces uncertainties in the classification of borderline galaxies. The division between E and S0 is a matter of definition and is made on the basis of the presence or absence of an outer amorphous envelope or thin fundamental plane surrounding the nuclear regions. The envelope appears to the eye as a change of the gradient of the $I(r)$ curve. The S0 gradient appears to be considerably smaller than for E nebulae, but this is subjective and must eventually be studied with microphotometer tracings.

The S0 are divided into three major subgroups, $S0_1$, $S0_2$, and $S0_3$. These subgroups represent extension along the sequence from early to late forms. The $S0_1$ is the most interesting from the dynamical standpoint because it represents the earliest of the class and is the nearest to the E forms. It is here that the first vestige of the thin fundamental plane appears. The distribution of light across the $S0_1$ is continuous, with no trace of absorption lanes or patches and no trace of structure. Except for the flatter intensity decrement, this type resembles E nebulae. Seven examples of $S0_1$ are shown in the atlas, six on page 4: NGC 1201, 3245, 3329, 4150, 4684, and 7457. All six are good type examples of intermediate to late $S0_1$. The envelopes in these systems are extensive. The earliest is 4684, where the envelope is not large compared with the nucleus; the latest is 1201. The remaining $S0_1$ illustrated is 4762, which is edge-on. This is one of the flattest galaxies known. The classification of $S0_1$ for this system is made on the basis of the intensity distribution along the spindle by analogy with 1201.

$S0_2$ galaxies show the same pattern of nucleus, lens, and envelope as the $S0_1$, but there is some structure in the envelope. On simple inspection, the lens appears to be surrounded by a relatively dark zone followed by a more luminous one. This description, however, represents a subjective interpretation of faint images and is deceptive. On photometric tracings, the luminosity gradients fall continually outward from the nuclei. The dark zone corresponds with a region in which the rate of fall first increases, then slows, and finally approximates the normal value. The form of the curve might be accounted for either by a circular ring of partial obscuration in the middle of the

envelope or by a concentration of luminosity near the boundary. Either explanation indicates a segregation of material. Five $S0_2$ are illustrated in the atlas, of which NGC 524 and 3065 are nearly face-on, and 4215, 4111, and 7332 are edge-on. The extreme weakness of the absorption features makes the characteristics of the $S0_2$ difficult to see on the photographic plates and nearly impossible to reproduce adequately. Consequently, they are not well shown in the atlas for NGC 524 or 3065. For 3065, a drawing is given on page 5 of the atlas showing the subjective $I(r)$ curve as the image appears on the photographic plate. Note how the outer sections seem to be segregated from the nuclear regions by the less luminous internal zone.

The weak absorption lane is silhouetted against the bright background of the nucleus in $S0_2$ galaxies seen edge-on. Because the ring is internal, the outer parts of the disk are unaffected and appear as bright ansae. Although the effect is rather inconspicuous because the internal obscuration is not opaque, it can be seen in NGC 4215, which is the best edge-on example. Here the nucleus and the outer regions of the fundamental plane are separated on each side by a zone of lower luminosity. If 4215 were seen face-on, it undoubtedly would resemble 3065. NGC 4111 is a second example of an $S0_2$ edge-on. Finally, 7332, shown on page 7, is a very early $S0_2$ on edge. The plate was overexposed so as to show the peculiar square-shaped nuclear region, but on weakly exposed plates, faint absorption lanes similar to those in 4215 appear close to the center.

Galaxies in the $S0_3$ subgroup exhibit a structureless envelope similar to that of the $S0_1$, but a sharp, narrow, absorption lane is found within the lens. The lane is in an arc concentric with the nucleus. The structure is a later and further developed form of the $S0_2$. The arc appears to lie in or near the fundamental plane, and it cannot usually be traced over a complete circle. The photographs suggest that the arc is buried in the lens, and is overlain by luminous material. Since the most conspicuous portions of the arc generally parallel the major axes of the projected images, the incompleteness of the circles might be accounted for by the orientation effect. Seven examples of $S0_3$ galaxies are shown in the atlas. The type examples are NGC 3032 and 4459,

11

shown on page 5. The internal absorption lane in 4459 is quite regular and can be traced through a complete circle. The lane in 3032 is less regular but is still circular. NGC 4526 is inclined greatly to the line of sight. The central lane is silhouetted against the nuclear region. Because of the high inclination, the lane cannot be traced through 360°. $S0_3$ galaxies seen on edge appear as further developed cases of 4215 [$S0_2$] and 4111 [$S0_2$]. The absorption band is seen as a dark lane blocking out the nuclear regions, and, because the ring is not peripheral, bright ansae appear. The finest example is NGC 4710, shown on page 6. The pattern can be reproduced by tipping the symmetry axis of 4459 [$S0_3$, page 5] through 90°. NGC 5866 is another good example. Two reproductions of this system are shown to illustrate the difficulty of separating $S0_2$ and $S0_3$ galaxies from E galaxies on overexposed or small-scale plates.

The transition between normal S0 and Sa galaxies is gradual. The absorption rings in $S0_2$ and $S0_3$ galaxies begin to deviate from circular patterns and take on a tightly wound spiral form. Two transitional galaxies are illustrated, 2855 [$S0_3$/Sa(r)] and 5273 [$S0_2$/Sa(r)]. The circular pattern in 2855 is broken, and absorption lanes begin to wind outward through the envelope. Because the beginnings of these embryo arms are tangent to an internal ring, the galaxy is of the (r) subtype. In 5273, faint spiral patterns of lower intensity wind outward from the nucleus. The pattern is faint and difficult to trace. The spiral pattern is of the (s) subtype.

Finally, five examples of peculiar S0 galaxies are illustrated in the atlas. The most nearly normal of the five are NGC 128 [$S0_1$pec] and NGC 7332 [$S0_2$pec]. The peculiar shape of the nuclear regions sets these apart from the normal $S0_1$ systems.

The third S0pec illustrated is NGC 2685, one of the most unusual galaxies in the entire sky. NGC 2685 has an elongated main body resembling $S0_1$ galaxies seen edge-on. In addition, a number of narrow bands appear to encircle the nucleus at right angles to the fundamental plane. The diameters of these circles are comparable with the diameter of the main body. The bands are faintly luminous. But in crossing the main body they appear to be re-

versed and are silhouetted against the bright background as narrow absorption lanes. Encircling the entire structure is a faint elliptical ring whose major axis coincides with that of the central regions. Inspection of the photographs suggests that the central region is shaped like a cigar rather than a disk or a pancake as in most other galaxies; that is to say, it may have the shape of a Jacobi ellipsoid rather than a Maclaurin spheroid.

The last two peculiar S0 galaxies illustrated are 3718 and 4753. NGC 3718 has a heavy bar of obscuration crossing the face. On plates taken with the 100-inch telescope, the underlying luminosity distribution is that of an $S0_1$ with a bright nucleus and an extended envelope. Hubble therefore called this system S0pec, because, if the absorbing lane were removed, a normal S0 would remain. On 200-inch and 48-inch Schmidt plates, however, two faint extensions to the envelope are seen which emerge from opposite sides of the periphery, suggesting spiral arms. The system looks somewhat like an SBb with the absorption lane constituting the bar. But the bars of all Sb galaxies are luminous, bright features, not absorption bands. The modern data, therefore, place NGC 3718 outside the classification scheme. Finally, NGC 4753 has numerous dark, irregular absorption bands crossing the face. If these were removed, the underlying luminosity distribution would be $S0_1$.

SUMMARY

1. The S0 class has three subtypes, $S0_1$, $S0_2$, and $S0_3$.

2. The $S0_1$ are transition objects from the E7 galaxies. The ellipticities of the central sections are flatter than those of E7. The distribution of light is continuous, with no trace of absorption lanes. The central regions resemble those of E galaxies, but the extensive outer envelope is flattened into a fundamental plane. The flat plane identifies the $S0_1$.

3. The $S0_2$ show the beginning of either a separation of material or a faint circular absorption pattern embedded in the envelope. Seen edge-on, the

internal pattern appears as decreased luminosity in a region intermediate between the nucleus and the edge of the envelope.

4. The $S0_3$ is a development from $S0_2$. A strong internal circular ring is present. The pattern is easily recognized in galaxies on edge. A dark central absorption lane blocks the nucleus, and bright ansae appear in the fundamental plane.

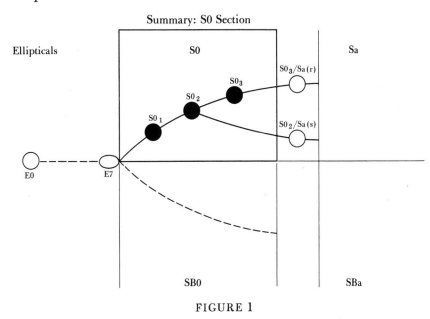

FIGURE 1

Sa GALAXIES

NORMAL spiral galaxies emerge from the S0 sequence with the appearance of noncircular absorption patterns and definite spiral arms. Although normal spirals show a wide diversity of form, they can be placed in a rough progressive order by three classification criteria: (1) the openness of the spiral arms, (2) the degree of resolution of the arms into stars, and (3) the relative size of the unresolved nuclear region.

On this basis, the spiral sequence is divided into the three subsections Sa, Sb, and Sc. There is a smooth transition between the sections, and the boundaries are somewhat arbitrary except at the two ends. In general terms, the type S0, from which the spiral sequence emerges, is characterized by a structureless lens and an extended envelope ($S0_1$) or by circular patterns of obscuration ($S0_2$, $S0_3$). The first true spirals are called Sa. They show tightly wound spiral patterns of obscuration, and they may or may not have tight spiral arms of luminous matter. The arms are invariably smooth, with no resolution into stars. Galaxies of type Sb have definite and pronounced spiral arms which, at the beginning of the section (Sab in an old notation), are tightly wound, and at the end become more massive and more open. Regular spiral dust lanes are a prominent feature of the Sb type. The dust is heavier and more conspicuous in Sb than in Sa systems.

The spiral structure dominates Sc galaxies. The arms are the most conspicuous part of the form. They are usually branched, highly resolved into stars, and open or unwound. Spiral dust lanes are a highly important feature of the spiral pattern, but they tend to be more irregular in the Sc than in the Sb systems.

For many years it was thought that the third classification criterion of the relative size of the unresolved nuclear region usually agreed with the criterion of the arms. Inspection of large numbers of photographs shows that, although there is a general correlation of the criteria, there are Sa galaxies (classified by criteria 1 and 2) that have small nuclear regions. The assignment of galaxies to the Sa, Sb, or Sc type is based here primarily on the characteristics of the arms. This does not mean that Sa galaxies do not exist with large amorphous central regions devoid of dust and spiral structure; all Sa galaxies of the 1302 type have this feature. We only wish to point out that a large amorphous central region is not a prerequisite for Sa galaxies.

The earliest galaxies of type Sa shown in the atlas are NGC 2681 [Sa(s)] and NGC 1302 [Sa(s)]. These galaxies have two sets of arms. The inner set is tightly wound about an amorphous central region. The arms are nearly circular and are difficult to trace except on short exposures. The inserts showing nuclear regions on page *9* of the atlas illustrate the feature. The inner arms of NGC 2681 appear to start tangent to the central nucleus, separated in their junction point to this nucleus by 180°. The arms can be traced for half a revolution where they lap back on each other and almost touch. They are so tightly wound that on casual inspection they appear to form a complete circular ring. The outer arms are multiple. They are difficult to trace because the texture is smooth and of low surface brightness. The arms can be interpreted as either fuzzy luminous filaments or as lanes of obscuring matter winding out through a smooth envelope. This confusion is illustrated by NGC 4378 on page *10* of the atlas. Here both interpretations are possible; either the spiral arms are the luminous filaments, or there are spiral dust lanes obscuring the smooth underlying surface. The evidence from NGC 6340 (not shown), which is a later galaxy of the NGC 1302 type, suggests that it is the luminous filaments that cause the arms.

Sa galaxies can be divided into two major groups, depending on the characteristics of the arms and of the nuclear regions. The NGC 1302 group has a rather large unresolved nuclear region with *multiple* arms starting tangent to the nuclear bulge. Seven examples are shown. All the galaxies on page *9* and the first three on page *10* are of this type. NGC 1302 is the earliest, 2775 is probably the latest, of the group. These multiple-arm Sa galaxies correspond to the NGC 2841, 7331 group of Sb galaxies, and the 628, M101 group of Sc galaxies. The group forms a predominant strain through the entire spiral sequence. The sequence can be arranged as 1302 (Sa) – 6340 (Sa) – 2775 (Sa) – 488 (Sb) – 2841 (Sb) – 5055 (Sbc) – 628 (Sc) – 1232 (Sc), where the arms become progressively more open proceeding from the Sa to the Sc. All these galaxies are shown in the atlas except 6340.

The second major group of Sa galaxies has predominantly small nuclei, and more or less regular thin internal dust lanes which usually set the pattern of the spiral. A few Sa galaxies have luminous spiral arms. The type example is NGC 4866 (page *11*). The extremes of the group are NGC 2811 (page *11*)

at the early end and 3623 (page *11*) at the late end. NGC 3623 is a very late Sa or early Sb. Here the dust lanes are conspicuous and the arms fairly open. All galaxies on page *11* are of the 4866 group. NGC 4941 on page *10* is another example of this group. Here the nucleus is very small. The tightly wound arms place this galaxy in the Sa class rather than in Sb or Sc. The arms are not completely smooth but are beginning to break up into small knots. NGC 4941 is a very late Sa, or, in an older notation, Sab. In general the spiral patterns of the second subgroup of Sa galaxies are formed by absorption lanes scattered over the main bodies. NGC 4293 (page *11*) shows this particularly well with heavy obscuration outlining the main features.

Within the 4866 major group we can separate a homogeneous subgroup of Sa galaxies with a special structural pattern, a typical example being NGC 4274 (page *12*). On short-exposure small-scale photographs, galaxies in this subgroup appear to have a narrow internal ring superimposed on the faint background of the envelope. On large-scale photographs, however, it appears that the ring is not complete but is broken at two diametrically opposite places, the pieces having drifted outward to form a spiral pattern. The departure from circularity is not great. This broken ring is connected to the nuclear region by two low-surface-brightness features. On good long-exposure plates the pattern of the spiral arms becomes quite evident, as is seen in the atlas reproduction of 4274. Notice how the two arms almost touch where the one sweeps through 180° and passes near the arm closer to the nucleus. Remnants of this "ring" structure are shown in NGC 3368 (page *12*), which is of later type and is seen more nearly perpendicular to the line of sight than 4274.

The last Sa galaxy shown is NGC 3081 on page *11*. It has a broken external ring of the type just described. The galaxy is similar to NGC 3185 (SBa, atlas page *43*) except that there is no strong bar connecting the ends of the broken ring. On long-exposure plates a faint bar can be traced in 3081, but its faintness puts this galaxy in the Sa rather than SBa class.

SUMMARY

1. Spiral arms first emerge in the Sa galaxies.

2. The Sa type covers a fairly large section of the spiral sequence. The early Sa have ill-defined arms which are smooth in texture and are tightly wound about the amorphous nuclear regions. The principal classification features are the nearly circular pattern of the arms and the lack of resolution in the arms. Late Sa have prominent dust lanes (e.g., 3623, page *11*) and a suggestion of lumpiness in the texture of the arms, showing the start toward resolution. Resolution begins in the early Sb systems and becomes "complete" in the Sc. But the arms are still tightly wound in the late Sa and form nearly circular patterns.

3. The nuclear regions of Sa galaxies can be either large (2775, page *10*) or small (4866, page *11*). There is not a unique connection between the relative size of the nuclear region and the arm pattern, but there does appear to be a strong correlation between the tightness of the spiral pattern and the lack of resolution of the arms into stars and H II regions.

Sb GALAXIES

THE differentiation of an intermediate class Sb between the early and late stages of the spiral sequence is necessarily arbitrary. The two ends of the sequence, Sa and Sc, are easy to define. The Sa spirals have incipient spiral arms which are usually smooth in texture and are tightly wound in nearly circular patterns about an amorphous central region. The Sc spirals have highly branched, well differentiated arms that are not tightly wound around the nucleus and are well resolved into stars and H II regions. There is much dust in the arms. The nuclear region is usually small and inconspicuous. The large number of galaxies falling between the two extremes are called Sb. Class characteristics are formulated in terms of intermediate criteria between the Sa and Sc. Although the separation may seem vague in principle it works well in practice.

There is considerable extension along the sequence from early Sb to late Sb, and classification at both extremes is difficult. In an older notation the transitional systems were called Sab and Sbc, but this finer division is not followed here.

The earliest example of Sb is NGC 4826, shown on page *13* of the atlas. Reproductions from a long- and a short-exposure photograph are given. On the longer exposure the vague, smooth, tight spiral pattern can be seen wound around a large, amorphous nuclear region. The short exposure shows much dust in the nucleus, and this is the feature that classifies NGC 4826 as an Sb rather than an Sa system. The latest Sb galaxies shown in the atlas are NGC 3627, 972, and 4433 on page *23*. These galaxies are not in a "linear sequence" from NGC 4826 but represent a different subgroup of Sb. That is to say, the classification sequence is not infinitely narrow perpendicular to the Sa ➤ Sb ➤ Sc direction, but has considerable width which is divided into subgroups. NGC 4826 is in one of the subgroups, and the three galaxies 972, 3627, and 4433 are in another. Nevertheless, the difference in the openness of the arms, the size of the amorphous nuclear region, and the amount and distribution of dust do illustrate change along the sequence of classification from early to late Sb.

The Sb spirals can be separated into two major divisions, corresponding to the 1302 and 4866 division of the Sa. Galaxies in the first division have relatively large amorphous nuclear regions. There are either two predominant arms as in NGC 4579 (page *13*) or a multiple-arm system as in 2841 (page *14*) and 488 (page *15*). All galaxies shown on pages *13* to *19* are of this type. Galaxies in the second major division of Sb are characterized by small nuclear regions with the typical Sb intermediate spiral pattern. All galaxies shown on pages *20* to *23* are of this type.

The Hubble Atlas

Two subgroups are recognized within the first major division. The first, called the 4569 subtype, has soft, thick arms, smooth in texture and of low surface brightness. The arms are tightly wound and may be bounded on their inner edges by dust lanes. The first five galaxies on page *13* are of this subtype. The Sc galaxy most like this group is M51, shown on page *26*.

The second subgroup of the large-nucleus type is comprised of galaxies like NGC 2841 or 488 and is known as 2841 type Sb. All galaxies shown on pages *14* to *19* are of this type. NGC 2841 has a large amorphous central region in which there is no spiral structure. This zone resembles an E or S0₁ galaxy. Many tightly wound spiral segments start tangent to the central zone and wind outward. At first glance the filaments appear to be complete spiral arms, but closer inspection shows that only thin, broken segments are present which cannot be traced as individual arcs for more than 30°. NGC 2841 is among the earliest of the group. The same pattern of amorphous central regions and tightly wound thin spiral segments is found in all the galaxies shown on page *15*. NGC 488 is a particularly good example. Here the segments of arms closest to the nucleus are smooth in texture. As the arms wind outward they become "lumpy" with evidence of condensations.

The form progresses through NGC 7217 (page *15*), where, on good plates taken with the 200-inch, the spiral arcs can be traced very close to a smaller amorphous nucleus. The reproduction in the atlas is overprinted and does not show this inner spiral pattern. The surface brightness of the spiral pattern increases toward the center, and the arms do not coalesce until they reach 3-mm radius from the center (on the scale of the atlas illustration). The arms can be traced even closer to the center in the magnificent spiral NGC 5055 (page *15*). Distinct spiral patterns can be traced to within 0.7-mm (radius) from the center of the atlas illustration of 5055.

But the curious thing about this galaxy and all others that follow in the sequence (3521, 4699, 1068, 4736, and 4800) is the sharp discontinuity of surface brightness of the spiral pattern in the inner region. The important point here is that, if these inner arms were to coalesce and to lose their identity as arms, the region would look amorphous, would have a high surface

brightness, and would appear like the structureless central regions of 488, 2841 of the Sb, and 2775 (page *10*), 3898 (page *10*), 2811 (page *11*), and 1302 (page *9*) of the Sa, and all members of the elliptical and S0₁ class.

From the geometrical forms alone we can place these closely coiled, multiple-arm galaxies in a sequence from Sc to Sa in the order: NGC 3810 (page *30*), 1232 (page *32*), M101 (page *27*), 628 (page *29*), 1068 (page *16*), 4699 (page *16*), 3521 (page *15*), 5055 (page *15*), 7217 (page *15*), 488 (page *15*), 2841 (page *14*), 2775 (page *10*), 3898 (page *10*), 2811 (page *11*), 6340, and 1302 (page *9*). In this order, the arms, starting tangent to the central amorphous bulge, become more tightly coiled, thinner, and more regular. And the nuclear region grows at the expense of the arms, the surface brightness of the central region remaining nearly constant whether it contains arms or is amorphous. This phenomenon may have evolutionary significance, suggesting that a given galaxy evolves from Sc to Sa owing to the kinematical condition of a differential velocity field and the absence of the formation of young O and B stars. These considerations will be discussed in detail elsewhere. The Sb galaxies forming this sequence are illustrated on pages *14*, *15*, and *16* of the atlas.

Three large-scale photographs of the near-by Sb galaxies of the multiple-arm type are shown on pages *17*, *18*, and *19*. The arms in NGC 7331 can be traced to within 6 mm of the center on the scale of the illustration. The burned-out portion in the illustration is not structureless. The arms of 7331 are much coarser than those of 5055 or 488. There are many Sb galaxies like 7331. NGC 4527 (shown by Hubble in the *Astrophysical Journal*, 97, 112, 1943) and NGC 4216 (atlas, page *25*, and also Hubble, *Ap. J.*, 97, 112, 1943) are examples. M31 on page *18* of this atlas has even coarser arms and a genuinely large amorphous nuclear region. Finally, M81 is shown. The arms here are thin and well defined. They begin tangent to the central region and wind outward for nearly 360° with only a slight departure from circularity. The dust arms can be traced throughout the central region of M81. They first appear at about 35 seconds of arc from the very bright central nucleus. This corresponds to 8 mm on the illustration on page *19* of the atlas.

16

In the second major subdivision of the Sb, the nuclear region is relatively small compared with the arm pattern. Fine subdivisions can be made among the many Sb systems in this group. The criteria are the thinness of the arms, the degree of organization of the luminous matter in the arms, and the degree of organization of the dust in the arms. Clearly the three galaxies shown in the top panels of page *20* belong to the same subgroup. Because the nuclear regions are large and the arms are thin and tightly wound, these systems are classified as Sb, but in structure they are similar to M101 of the Sc. The three galaxies in the lower panels of page *20* also seem to form a subgroup. Here the arms appear to be disorganized, with dust scattered somewhat irregularly over the face. These galaxies may be the Sb counterpart of the Sc group characterized by NGC 253, NGC 2903, and the galaxies on pages *30, 34,* and *35* of the Sc section.

Galaxies of an interesting special subgroup are shown on page *21*. They are characterized by the presence of an internal ring from which the outer spiral arms emerge. These galaxies, especially NGC 3705, resemble the 4274 group of Sa, in which a broken internal ring is a prominent feature. Faint outer arms present in NGC 4750, 4580, and 4725 are shown in the negative inserts.

Another special subgroup, called NGC 210 galaxies, is shown on page *22*. Each of these galaxies has an internal and an external set of arms, but the arms of each set appear to be of different pitch. The best example is NGC 210 itself. Two tightly wound dust arms are present in the central nuclear region. Springing from opposite ends of this region are two arms with open pitch and partial resolution into knots. The same pattern is repeated in NGC 1964, 615, and 23. The arms in the nuclear region are almost circular and are smoother in texture than the outer arms. Furthermore, the central arms are more clearly outlined by the dust than by luminous patterns.

The final subtype of Sb illustrated in the atlas, on page *23*, has NGC 3627 and NGC 4433 as its prototypes. Here the face of the galaxy is dominated by a rather chaotic dust pattern forming the spiral structure. The classification is Sb, because the arms are not very open nor is there great resolution of the arms into knots and stars as in the Sc systems. There is too much dust with disorganized patterns to call these galaxies Sa.

Sc GALAXIES

DOMINANCE of multiple spiral arms and small amorphous nuclear regions are the characteristics of Sc galaxies. These features and the high degree of resolution of the open, branched-arm system make Sc galaxies easy to recognize. The detection of resolution in spiral arms depends on distance and on telescope size, but in practice the 60-inch, 100-inch, and 200-inch telescopes give photographs of sufficient scale so that either individual knots (H II regions and associations of stars) or a general lumpiness in the texture of the arms can be detected in galaxies with redshifts as large as 15,000 km/sec. All the near-by bright galaxies are within this limit.

The Sc galaxies exhibit great diversity in form. At least six major subgroups can be distinguished. These groups in general represent development along the sequence of classification from early to late Sc. The largest subgroup of Sc galaxies resembles M101 (page *27*). The arms are thin, multiply branched, and loosely wound about a very small nuclear region. They can be traced through about one revolution, although in some galaxies, such as NGC 5364 (page *32*), segments of the main arms make nearly two complete turns. But this is rare. Although most Sc galaxies have multiple arms, close inspection of the photographs shows that only two predominant arms emerge from opposite sides of the nuclear region. They wind outward for nearly half a revolution, at which point they branch into many individual segments which continue to spiral outward to form the multiple structure. M101 is a particularly good example of this (page *27*). The beginning of the two major arms in the central region is shown in the enlarged print of the nucleus on page *31*.

17

Here the arms begin as dust lanes, lying within a few hundred parsecs of the center of the galaxy, on the inside edge of the luminous matter. The situation is shown even better for M100, where the dust lanes spiral through about 120° very close to the nucleus (upper panel, page *31*) and then change into the prominent luminous arms farther out (page *28*). (The negative reproduction of M100 in the *Astrophysical Journal*, *127*, 513, figure 8, shows the central regions well.)

Nine examples of the M101-type Sc systems are illustrated in the atlas. The type example, M101, is shown on page *27*. It is an intermediate Sc about midway between early Sc and late Sc. M100 and M83 illustrate dispersion within the group. M100 is an early Sc, called Sbc in an earlier notation. M83 is a transitional example between normal Sc and SBc. The two major dust lanes threading into the nucleus from opposite sides of M83 are characteristic of the SBb galaxies. The bar is not pronounced, however, and M83 is classed as Sc/SBc rather than SBc. Note how the dust lanes in both M100 and M83 lie on the inside of the luminous arms. This appears to be characteristic of all galaxies. Other M101-type galaxies illustrated are NGC 628, 4254, 4303, 1084, 6181, and 157. NGC 628 (page *29*) clearly resembles M101 in the arm structure but differs in the nuclear region. The dust lanes do not begin at the center of NGC 628 but start tangent to a small amorphous nuclear region (see page *31*, lower right panel). Similar beginnings of the dust arms occur in NGC 5194 (M51, page *31*, upper right panel). M51 may be of the M101 subgroup, although the arms are thick and ill defined. This galaxy resembles the NGC 4569 subtype of Sb (page *13*), with soft, thick arms which are rather smooth in texture. The closest match is NGC 4579 (Sb), but M51 is considerably later in type and has more dust on the inner side of the luminous arms.

Other types of Sc galaxies exist besides the M101 group. The prototype galaxies for a second major subgroup of Sc are NGC 5364 (page *32*) and NGC 309 (page *32*), which have multiple spiral arms that start tangent to an external circular ring of luminous matter. This subgroup is the Sc counterpart of the "ringed" Sb spirals of the NGC 3705 (page *21*) and 1832 (page *21*) type, and the "ringed" Sa spirals of the 4274 (page *12*) type.

Examples of the third major subgroup of Sc galaxies are shown on page *30* of the atlas. The prototype galaxy of this group is NGC 1637. Here the arms are not so well defined as in the M101 group. The arms generally start in the nucleus and cover the entire face of the galaxy. Usually they are not well separated and are more difficult to trace than arms in M101 type systems. NGC 3810 (page *30*, upper left panel) is an early example of this type. The arms can be traced to within 6 seconds of arc from the center of NGC 3810 (2 mm on the scale of the illustration). The high-intensity central region (containing the inner arms) is similar to that in galaxies described in the NGC 1068 group of Sb (1068, 4699, 3521, 5055, 7217, 488, and 2841). There may be evolutionary significance to this sequence, with the evolution proceeding in the Sc to Sa direction. The NGC 1637 subgroup is considered to be more advanced along the Sc section than galaxies in the M101 group, for the arm pattern is not so well defined in NGC 1637. The subgroup is midway between the M101 and the NGC 253 groups described below.

NGC 253 (page *34*) is a spectacular object. It is very large in angular size and is probably located just beyond the Local Group. The spiral pattern is more difficult to trace than in either the M101 or 1637 groups because of the ill-defined arms and the large internal obscuration caused by dust scattered more or less chaotically across the disk. The arms in galaxies of this group are broad, multiple, and usually highly resolved into knots. Six galaxies of the 253 group are shown on page *35*. The illustration of NGC 2903 unfortunately does not show the very complicated internal obscuring pattern across the entire face, but this feature is shown to advantage in the remaining five galaxies of page *35*.

In a fifth group of Sc systems are galaxies of the M33, NGC 2403 type. Both these systems are near enough to be highly resolved. M33 is a member of the Local Group. Its distance modulus is about $m - M = 24.5$. If the 200-inch can photograph to $m_{pg} = 23.0$, then plates of M33 reach $M_{pg} = -1.5$. NGC 2403 is in the M81 group whose modulus is about $m - M = 27.1$. Here stars brighter than $M_{pg} = -4.1$ are resolved. The spiral arms in both these galaxies are not well defined, but the general spiral pattern is quite evident. Seen at a greater distance, the arms would appear to be thick and loosely coiled.

The transition between very late Sc and Irr is gradual. There are a number of galaxies whose spiral arms can still be traced but in which the arm pattern is very chaotic and ill defined. These systems have been called Sd by Shapley and very late Sc by Hubble. Four examples of such systems are illustrated on page *37* of the atlas. The group is designated as the NGC 4395 group. Note the very low surface brightness of all four galaxies. Various sections of the galaxy shown in the upper right panel of page *37* are catalogued in the NGC as separate objects. The entire galaxy is known as NGC 4395, 4399, 4400, and 4401. Because of the low surface brightness of this and of NGC 45, the photographic contrast was increased in the reproductions by printing from a copy negative.

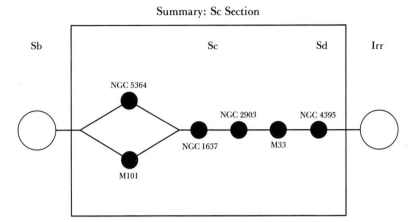

FIGURE 2

SUMMARY

1. Sc galaxies have very small amorphous central regions. The spiral-arm pattern dominates the structural form on photographs taken in blue light.

2. Nearly all Sc galaxies have multiple spiral arms loosely wound around the central regions. Two principal arms can generally be traced almost to the very center of the system. Multiple branching creates new arms from the two "parent" arms. The branching occurs after the parent arms have wound outward for about 90°.

3. The arms show a very high degree of resolution into knots, which are mostly H II regions and associations of stars.

4. There is much dust in the spiral arms; usually it lies on the inside of the luminous arcs. Dust arms are traceable into the nuclear regions (see the illustrations of M100, M51, M101, and NGC 628 on page *31*).

5. There is great variation of structural form along the section from early Sc to late Sc. Six major subgroups are recognized on the basis of the cleanness of the arm separation. (There is very clear arm separation in the M101 group, and very poor in the NGC 2903, M33, and NGC 4395 groups.) The

division into subgroups, although perhaps somewhat artificial, illustrates the progression along the sequence. The progression is shown in figure 2.

6. The transition from late Sc to Irr is smooth. NGC 4395–4401, NGC 45, and NGC 5204 are transition examples.

IRREGULAR GALAXIES

IRREGULAR galaxies comprise 2.8 per cent of the galaxies north of $\delta = -15°$ brighter than $m_{pg} = 13.0$. Irregular systems divide sharply into two groups. Galaxies of the first group are highly resolved into luminous O and B stars and H II regions. The systems show no circular symmetry about a rotational axis. Prominent spiral structure is missing. These galaxies form a continuation of the late Sc forms of the NGC 4395 type (page *37*). The type examples are the Large and Small Magellanic Clouds. Galaxies of the first type are called Irr I. Galaxies of the second group also show no rotational symmetry. The photographic images are completely smooth in texture, show no sign of resolution into stars, and are often crossed by irregular absorption dust lanes and patches. These systems are called Irr II. The type example for the group is M82 (page *41*).

Thirteen Magellanic Cloud-type irregulars (Irr I) are shown in the atlas on pages *38*, *39*, and *40*. Three irregulars of the M82 type (Irr II) are illustrated on page *41*. A fourth Irr II system is NGC 5195, which is the companion to M51 (page *26*).

The picture of the Large Magellanic Cloud given on page *38* was taken with the Mount Wilson 10-inch refractor by Dr. Karl Henize in South Africa. The plate was red-sensitive and shows the numerous hydrogen-emission regions in the LMC. The six galaxies on page *39* and the first four on page *40* are all good examples of the Irr I type. Note the lack of circular symmetry in all, the extreme resolution into stars, the large number of H II regions, the lack of spiral structure, and the lack of obvious dust lanes or patches. All ten of these galaxies are near-by systems. IC 1613 (page *40*) and the Sextans System (page *39*) are members of the Local Group. Ho II, NGC 2366, and IC 2574 are members of the M81 group, and the remainder of the systems are no farther from us than the near-by Virgo Cluster of galaxies.

The last two irregulars shown on page *40* are either dwarf spirals or irregulars (the plates are not good enough to tell which) in the NGC 1023 group of galaxies comprising the Andromeda group (NGC 891, 925, 1003, 1023, 1058, and possibly 1156; see Humason, Mayall, and Sandage, *Astronomical Journal*, *61*, 97, 1956, table XI on page 144). These are very low-surface-brightness objects in a group of seven dwarf systems connected with this Andromeda aggregate. They were found on the 48-inch Schmidt plates in a special search of this aggregate for dwarf members.

Galaxies of type Irr II present a mystery. Three reproductions of M82, made from plates of different exposure times, are shown on page *41*. No hint of resolution into stars is present, although the distance modulus is $m - M =$ 27.1. Any stars brighter than $M_{pg} = -4.0$ should be observed. (Compare M82 with M81. Both are at the same distance.) The color index of M82 is $C_p = 0.81$ (Holmberg, *Medd. Lunds Astr. Obs.*, ser. II, no. 136, 1958), but the spectrum is A5 (Humason et al., *Astronomical Journal*, *61*, 97, 1956). Dust lanes are evident across the entire face of M82. NGC 3077, which probably forms a dynamical companion to M82, and NGC 5195, the companion to M51, are of similar form. Finally, NGC 520 has a smooth texture to the photographic image and, for this reason, is placed with the Irr II group.

BARRED SPIRALS

INTRODUCTION*

THE class of galaxies characterized by a bar across the central regions was first recognized by H. D. Curtis, who assigned to it the provisional name "ϕ type" spirals. Later the more convenient term "barred" spirals, represented by the symbol SB, was suggested by Hubble and has been universally adopted. The SB class includes 15 per cent of the brighter galaxies. The members do not differ systematically from normal spirals either in luminosity, dimension, spectral characteristics, or distribution over the sky.

*The material in this introduction rests heavily upon notes left by Hubble. The change from the 1936 system of classification to the present system, namely, the introduction of the new SB0 class, is discussed here for the first time.

In describing the barred spirals it will be convenient to differentiate (1) the nucleus, (2) a region concentric with the nucleus which has the shape of a convex lens seen in projection, (3) a ring of luminous matter which when present lies on the rim of the lens and in the progression of the (r) subtype develops into the spiral arms, and (4) the envelope or outer region of the galaxy. In addition, there is always present the characteristic feature of the class, a more or less well defined luminous bar extending centrally across the lens and terminating at its rim or on the innermost coils of the spiral arms.

The structural features fall into a sequence in which a simple pattern of bar and ring develops into a pattern of bar and spiral arms. In several respects, such as the unwinding of the arms and their progressive resolution, the sequence resembles that of normal spirals and, like the normal spirals, was originally subdivided into the three distinct sections SBa, SBb, and SBc in the classification of 1936. Hubble found the scheme useful for certain purposes, but evidence accumulated from large-scale photographs between 1936 and 1950 demonstrated a rather serious defect. The subdivisions in the parallel sequences of normal and barred spirals were not comparable, because those galaxies classified SBa showed no spiral arms whatsoever whereas the Sa galaxies were true spirals with the beginnings of real arms. Galaxies classed as SBa according to the 1936 scheme were similar to the new class of transition galaxies, called S0, which Hubble had isolated between the E7 and the Sa systems. The SBa galaxies (1936 style) were the transition objects from the lenticular galaxies E7 to the true barred spirals, much as the S0 galaxies furnished the transition between E7 and Sa. Thus the parallel sequences of galaxies with true spiral arms were represented by two sections (SBb and SBc) in the barred spirals and by three sections (Sa, Sb, and Sc) in the normal spirals. Hubble changed his original classification system to correct this difficulty by adding a new class called SB0. If the bar were removed from galaxies in this class, an S0 galaxy would result. It therefore became clear that the objects previously classed as SBa corresponded more closely to the S0 systems than to the Sa galaxies along the normal spiral sequence. Consequently, those galaxies called SBa in the 1936 system have been renamed SB0 and the remaining barred spirals have been redistributed among the three sections SBa, SBb, and SBc.

SB0 GALAXIES

THE SB0 class represents a transitional stage between the elliptical galaxies and the true barred spirals. In this respect, the class is similar to S0 in the sequence of normal spirals. The boundary of the SB0 is defined on the E side by the presence of the characteristic bar and on the SBa side by the absence of spiral arms. Features common to the entire class are a nucleus, a lens of lower intensity concentric with the nucleus, the bar which usually terminates on the periphery of the lens, and occasionally an outer envelope and/or an external ring. The bar can be either very indistinct and difficult to recognize or well developed and prominent. The development of the bar is interpreted as a progression along the sequence from early to late SB0, and is recognized in the classification by the subdivision into three groups $SB0_1$, $SB0_2$, and $SB0_3$.

The $SB0_1$, the earliest subclass, is distinguished by a broad and poorly defined region of enhanced luminosity which crosses the central lens at some arbitrary angle to the major axis of the nucleus and lens. This enhanced region *is* the bar of $SB0_1$. The bars are indistinct and difficult to trace on small-scale plates. Consequently, observers with small telescopes will probably confuse $SB0_1$ and $S0_1$ galaxies. The earliest examples of $SB0_1$ in the Shapley-Ames catalogue are 1023 and 4435, neither of which is shown in the atlas. NGC 4612 (page *42*) is the only $SB0_1$ illustrated, and its features are rather difficult to see in the illustration. A sketch of the galaxy is shown in the legend; the nucleus, the lens, and the broad inclined region of enhanced luminosity should be noted. This is a type example of SB0$_1$. The inclined region in SB0$_1$ galaxies later than NGC 4612 narrows and becomes more distinct until, in the SB0$_2$ and SB0$_3$, the bar is prominent.

SB0$_2$ galaxies have a nucleus, a lens, and a bar. The bar is *not* continuous from the nucleus to the rim of the lens. It consists of the central nucleus plus two regions of enhanced luminosity at diametrically opposite points of the periphery of the lens. NGC 2859 (page *42*) is the type example, with 4262 (page *42*) and 2950 (page *42*) as members of the group. All three are illustrated in the atlas. External rings are common in the SB0$_2$ and SB0$_3$. NGC 2859 is a particularly good example. It is classed as SB0$_2$(R) in an obvious notation where (R) designates the existence of the external ring.

SB0$_3$ galaxies have bars extending entirely across the face of the lens. This is a development of the partial bars of the SB0$_2$. No examples of pure SB0$_3$ are shown in the atlas. The central regions of NGC 4643 [SB0$_3$/SBa(r)] (page *42*) and NGC 5101 [SB0$_3$/SBa(s)] (page *42*), however, illustrate the SB0$_3$ characteristics. Here the bar is intense and well developed, and it contributes the major part of the luminosity of the system. Both NGC 4643 and 5101 show incipient spiral structure which puts them in a transition class to SBa. The outer regions of 4643 contain arms starting tangent to a complete ring at the rim of the lens. In NGC 5101, the ring is broken at the ends of the bar. This broken ring is an early development of a structure that will become bona fide arms in the SBa class. The arms spring from the tips of the bar instead of from a complete internal ring. NGC 4643 and 5101 are the earliest examples of two parallel developments of spiral types which are characterized by galaxies NGC 1398 [SBb(r)] (arms starting tangent to an internal ring) and NGC 1300 [SBb(s)] (arms springing from the ends of the bar). The difference in the starting place of the arms between 4643 and 5101 appears to be fundamental and will be stressed in the later classification. These two lines of development can be traced along the entire barred sequence from SBa to SBc and also along the normal spiral sequence from Sa to Sc. The notation for the types where the arms start tangent to a ring (like 1398) is a lower-case (r) after the main type symbol. The notation for the types where the arms spring

from the bar (like 1300) is a lower-case (s) after the main type symbol. Thus the outer part of NGC 4643 is classed as SBa(r) and that of 5101 as SBa(s).

SUMMARY

1. There are three subtypes, SB0$_1$, SB0$_2$, and SB0$_3$, which differ from one another in the characteristics of the bar.

2. The bar of SB0$_1$ galaxies is a broad, indistinct region whose surface brightness is higher than that of the surrounding lens. It is inclined at a random angle to the major axis of the projected image.

3. The bar of SB0$_2$ galaxies does not extend completely across the face of the underlying lens. There are two diametrically opposite regions of enhanced luminosity on the rim of the lens which, together with the nucleus, constitute the bar.

4. The bar of SB0$_3$ galaxies extends completely across the face of the lens. It is narrow, well defined, and bright.

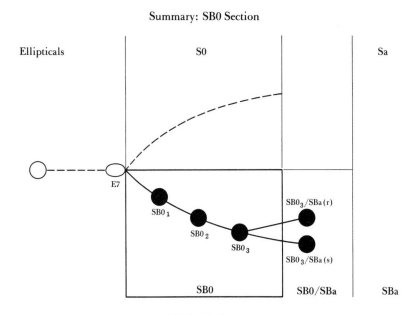

Summary: SB0 Section

FIGURE 3

SBa GALAXIES

THE SBa is the earliest of the true barred-spiral forms. There is a spread along the sequence from early to late SBa which is recognized by the developing characteristics of the spiral arms. The arms of the early SBa are poorly defined, smooth in texture, broad, and fuzzy. They are usually coiled in a nearly circular pattern around a central region which itself closely resembles the nucleus, lens, and bar of the SB0₃. The earliest of the SBa is NGC 936 [SBa(s)], which is not shown in the atlas because of the difficulty of reproducing the very faint arms. The earliest SBa illustrated is NGC 7743 [SBa(s)] (page *43*). Here the arms are insignificant relative to the nuclear regions; they are smooth in texture and closely wound. There is no trace of resolution. In the later SBa, the arms are relatively narrow and well developed, and some show beginning traces of resolution (NGC 3185, page *43*; 175, page *43*). The arms here are tightly wound and form nearly circular arcs that appear in projection as elliptical loops.

The spiral pattern can originate in two ways, either by emerging tangent to a complete internal ring at the edge of the lens, as in NGC 5566 [SBa(r), page *43*], or by springing from the ends of the bar, as in NGC 175 [SBa(r), page *43*] and NGC 3185 [SBa(s), page *43*]. As was mentioned in the section on the SB0, these two lines of development are designated (r) and (s), respectively. The two types can be traced throughout the sequence of later forms.

Six examples of SBa are given in the atlas on pages *43* and *44*: NGC 175 [SBa(s)], NGC 2217 [SBa(r)], NGC 3185 [SBa(s)], NGC 5566 [SBa(r)], NGC 7743 [SBa(s)], and the peculiar object NGC 4314 [SBa(s)pec].

Descriptions of the six examples will illustrate the features of the class. NGC 2217 is shown in both positive and negative prints. This galaxy has a well developed nucleus, a lens, and a bar of the SB0₃ type. The bar extends to the rim of the lens, on which very faint beginnings of spiral arms are found.

These arms start at diametrically opposite points of the rim about 15° around from the termination point of the bar. Consequently 2217 is of the (r) class, although it is a poor example. Casual inspection would suggest that the nearly circular outer parts of the arms form a closed ring separated from the nucleus. But this is not so, because there are broad, faint rim connections which join onto these brighter, outer regions of the arms at almost a 90° angle. This pattern of arms is almost identical to that of NGC 3185 [SBa(s)]. The difference in appearance is an effect of projection. NGC 3185 is inclined considerably to the line of sight, whereas 2217 is nearly face-on. This projection effect makes the two separate arms more easily visible in 3185 than in 2217. In both galaxies, the arms are very closely coiled and appear to form a closed ring, but close inspection reveals that there are indeed two separate arms which spring from the ends of the bar. Each arm can be traced through 180° until it passes near, and almost joins, the opposite end of the bar. Each arm does pass beyond the other, and each can be traced on the outside of the beginning of the other arm. The same pattern would be produced if the ring had broken away from the bar (just above the bar at one end, and just below at the other) and the broken ends of the ring had drifted outward. This form, which can be traced in NGC 3185 and 2217, can also be seen in NGC 175 and 7743. NGC 3081, a transition between Sa and SBa, shows the same pattern. In NGC 175 the arms are slightly more open than in 2217 or in 7743, and this fact, together with the partial resolution of the arms into knots, places 175 as the latest SBa(s) of the group. The division between SBa and SBb is rather arbitrary, with 175 close to the boundary. In an earlier notation, NGC 175 was called SBab.

The galaxy NGC 5566 is the only good example in the Shapley-Ames catalogue of an SBa(r) north of δ=−30° brighter than m_{pg}=13.0. The insert of NGC 5566 shows that the broad fuzzy arms emerge tangent to the internal ring characteristic of the (r) subdivision. Two thin dust lanes in the middle of the arms are silhouetted against the luminous background. The appearance of these lanes in the arms of 5566 is significant, for they mark the beginnings of features that can be traced in the later stages of the classification.

23

One of the major characteristics of the SBb(s) is the presence of two dust lanes leaving the nucleus one on each side of the bar and extending into the spiral arms. This feature is conspicuously absent in all SBa. The bars of most SBa's are devoid of dust. There is one exception, NGC 4314 [SBa(s)pec], which is illustrated on page *44*. This peculiar object has internal spiral arms opening in the same direction as the external arms. The space between the luminous spiral pattern may be dust lanes in analogy with the almost identical pattern in the nucleus of NGC 4321 (M100) [Sc] shown on page *31*. A similar but less pronounced internal structure of this same sort may be present in NGC 4245 [SBa].

The final object illustrated in this section of the atlas is NGC 4691 [SBa (pec)], which is included with 4314 to show that absorption does occur rarely in other objects. But here the dust is in a quite irregular pattern in contrast to the regular form in 4314. Hubble classed 4691 as SBapec; on the basis of the 200-inch plate shown, I should now classify this galaxy as an Irregular of the M82 type.

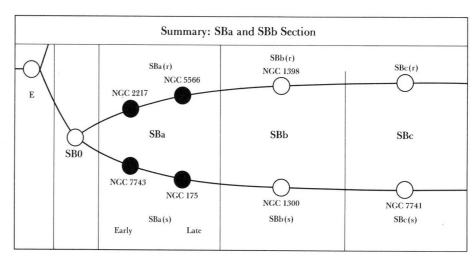

FIGURE 4

SBb GALAXIES

SUMMARY

1. The characteristic bar is prominent and smooth in texture with no trace of resolution into knots or stars. No dust lanes are present in the bar as in SBb(s).

2. Spiral arms first appear in the SBa. They are usually closely coiled about the central lens and bar; they are often faint and inconspicuous, and usually smooth in texture although traces of partial resolution begin in the very late SBa.

3. The arms can either begin tangent to an internal ring [(r) subtype], or can spring from the ends of the bar [(s) subtype]. This division into (r) and (s) groups is not prominent in the SBa but is a dominant feature of SBb and SBc galaxies.

THE classification criteria for the SBb are intermediate between those of the SBa and the SBc. They are based primarily on the openness and the degree of resolution of the spiral arms, and on the complete lack of resolution of the bar. The SBb galaxies break rather sharply into two subgroups, depending on whether the spiral arms start tangent to an internal ring [the (r) subtype] or spring from the ends of the bar [the (s) subtype]—the same two basic subgroups that have been discussed throughout this atlas.

The prototype SBb(s) galaxy is NGC 1300, shown on page *45*. The intense nuclear region of the bar is small. The entire bar with the exception of the very tips is smooth in texture with no hint of resolution into stars. This completely amorphous structure is so similar to the central regions of near-by

Sb galaxies (M31, M81, etc.) that it appears likely that no stars brighter than $M_V \approx -3$ are present in the bar of NGC 1300. This assumption is perhaps a bit conjectural because the estimated distance modulus is $m - M = 31.6$ (based on a Hubble constant of 75 km/sec 10^6 parsecs). Lack of resolution with the 200-inch telescope means only that there are no stars brighter than $M_{pg} \approx -8.6$. The fact, however, that the color index of the small central nucleus is 0.54 (Pettit, *Astrophysical Journal*, *120*, 413, 1954) suggests the presence of old stars (like a globular cluster or an elliptical galaxy). There are two straight dust lanes in NGC 1300 which emerge from the nucleus and proceed on opposite sides of the bar. These absorption features bend sharply at the termination of the bar and continue on the inside of the spiral arms. The high-surface-brightness parts of the arms can be traced through about 180°. The arms continue for another half revolution, but with much lower intensity. They can be traced for a total of about 360°. These features in NGC 1300 are characteristic of all SBb(s) galaxies. Four additional SBb(s) systems are shown on page *46* of the atlas. There is no sharp division between the normal spiral sequence and the barred sequence, because many transition galaxies exist. M83, shown on page *28*, is an example of an Sc/SBb(s). It has more of the features of an Sc than of an SBb galaxy, but the characteristic absorption lanes and the suggestion of a bar are evident. The four galaxies on page *46* illustrate the transition between pure SBb(s) [NGC 5383] and SBb(s)/Sb [NGC 6951]. Note the two straight absorption lanes across the face of the bar, the spiral pattern springing at right angles from the ends of the bar, and the nearly circular arm pattern.

The prototype of the ringed subgroup of the barred spirals, SBb(r), is NGC 1398, shown on page *47*. Note how the outer spiral arms start tangent to a narrow internal "ring." The ring is actually not complete but is composed of very tightly wound spiral segments which are thin and well defined. The outer arms are highly branched and of very low surface brightness. There are no absorption features in the bar. Indeed, no SBb(r) galaxy in the Mount Wilson collection has the straight absorption lanes so characteristic of SBb(s).

Galaxies exist that are intermediate in type between the (s) and (r) sub-groups. They are designated by (sr) if they are closer to the (s) type, or by (rs) if closer to the (r) type. NGC 4394 [SBb(sr)] is an example. The arms spring from the ends of the bar, but they spiral rather tightly, forming an almost closed ring. The feature is similar, but of later type, to the spiral pattern in NGC 3185 SBa(s) (page *43*) and to 7743 SBa(s) (page *43*).

Four galaxies are shown on page *48* which illustrate the pure SBb(r) type [NGC 2523] and the transition cases SBb(rs) and SBb(sr). Note in each the smooth texture of the bar and the well defined arms.

SUMMARY

1. SBb galaxies have a well defined bar structure which is smooth in texture with no hint of resolution into stars.

2. There are two subgroups. The spiral arms of the SBb(s) group spring from the end of the bar at right angles. Two straight dust lanes in the bar turn sharply at the end of the bar and follow the inside of the spiral arms. NGC 1300 is the prototype. The spiral arms of the SBb(r) group start tangent to an internal ring on which the bar terminates. No dust lanes are present in the bar. NGC 1398 and NGC 2523 are prototypes of this group.

3. Transition objects exist between the (s) and (r) subgroups (e.g., NGC 4593 and NGC 4548), and between the SBb(s) and Sb type (e.g., M83, NGC 1097, and NGC 6951).

SBc GALAXIES

THE characteristics of SBc galaxies are (1) the high degree of resolution of the bar and of the spiral arms into knots and luminous lumps, and (2) the openness of the spiral arms.

Six SBc galaxies are shown on page *49* of this atlas. As in the SBb, the SBc can be separated into the two subgroups (r) and (s), although the *pure* ringed type is not common. Most central rings are broken into several segments. An example is NGC 1073 (page *49*), where the ring is not complete but breaks about 30° from either end of the bar. Of the six galaxies illustrated, three are of the pure SBc(s) type and three are of the combination type [SBc(sr)].

Note the high degree of resolution into stars of NGC 7741. Both the arms and the bar are resolved into knots. This feature of the resolution of the bar is unique to the SBc type. The bars in SBa and SBb galaxies are smooth in texture, with no hint of resolution.

Relation of S and SB Sequences

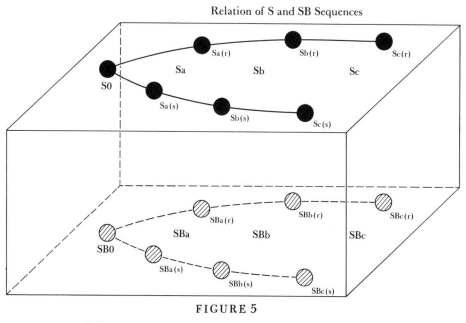

FIGURE 5

26

Preface to the Illustrations

ONE hundred seventy-six separate galaxies are illustrated. The reproductions have been made from plates in the Mount Wilson–Palomar plate collection. The original negatives were obtained with either the 60- or the 100-inch telescope on Mount Wilson, or with the 200-inch reflector or the 48-inch Schmidt telescope on Palomar Mountain.

Technical data for each negative are given in the legend on the page facing the illustration. Each galaxy is identified by either its NGC number, its Messier number, or its special designation; to the right of the galaxy designation is the nebular classification. The north and west directions are indicated by arrows in the upper right-hand corner of the legend. Below the NGC designation is the plate number of the original negative. The prefix of the plate number identifies the telescope, and the suffix identifies the observer responsible for the negative. In the prefix, PH stands for Palomar Hale; PS, Palomar Schmidt; H, the 100-inch; S, the 60-inch. The suffix letters of the plate number stand for the observer. The code is: B=Baade, Bm=Baum, Δ=Duncan, H=Hubble, Mi=Minkowski, MH=Humason, P=Pease, Ri=Ritchey, S= Sandage. For example, a plate labeled PH–116–H was taken with the 200-inch by Hubble.

One hundred thirteen plates of the atlas were taken with the 200-inch, 54 with the 100-inch, 16 with the 60-inch, 2 with the 48-inch, and 1 with the Mount Wilson 10-inch telescope.

The date when the plate was taken is given below the plate number. The emulsion type plus filter (if any) appears under the date. Most of the plates were sensitive to blue light ($\lambda\lambda 3300$–5000), but some negatives were obtained with yellow- or red-sensitive emulsions. A variety of plate types were used in the early days, such as Eastman 40, Agfa Blue, Cramer High Speed Special, Imperial Eclipse, Seed 30, and Seed 23. These names are abbreviated in the descriptions. Since the war, the blue plates have been Eastman 103aO or Eastman IIaO. The blue filters have been Schott WG2 or Schott GG13. Eastman 103aD plates were used for the yellow-green region of the spectrum, and 103aE plates for the red-Hα region. Schott GG11 and either a Schott RG1, RG2, or a red plexiglass filter were used with these plates.

The exposure time of the plates is stated on the next line. Notice that plates taken in the early days had very long exposure times, whereas modern blue plates with the 200-inch are generally exposed for only 30 minutes. This difference illustrates the great increase in speed of photographic materials between 1910 and 1956.

The final datum in the list is the enlargement factor of the reproduction from the original plate. The quoted values are accurate to about 5 per cent. The scale of the reproduction in seconds of arc per millimeter is stated for each galaxy in the following table. It can be computed from the enlargement factor and from the scale of the appropriate telescope. The telescope scales are 11$\farcs$06/mm for the 200-inch, 16$\farcs$00/mm for the 100-inch, 27$\farcs$12/mm for the 60-inch, and 67$\farcs$00/mm for the 48-inch Schmidt.

Below the data, a few lines of text describe each galaxy illustrated. Information therein notes features of the images which are present on the original plates but which may be lost in the reproduction. Also, the relation of the particular galaxy to the entire classification scheme is sometimes indicated.

The Hubble Atlas

Distance moduli are given for a few objects, quoted as apparent magnitude minus absolute magnitude. The relation of $m - M$ to the distance r in parsecs is $\log r = 0.2(m - M + 5)$. Most of the values for the moduli were determined from the redshifts observed by either Humason or Mayall (*Astronomical Journal*, *61*, 97, 1956) together with an assumed rate of expansion of 75 km/sec per 10^6 parsecs (Sandage, *Astrophysical Journal*, *127*, 513, 1958). These distances are not accurate for galaxies whose redshifts are smaller than 1000 km/sec, because the random motions (of the order of 200 km/sec) form an appreciable fraction of the systematic redshift values, causing a rather large error in the computed distance for near-by galaxies.

The following table provides an index of the galaxies illustrated in the atlas. The objects are listed by NGC number. The telescope used, the galaxy type, the page of the atlas on which the galaxy is iullstrated, the enlargement, and the scale of the print in seconds of arc per millimeter are given.

Table of Data for Galaxies in the Atlas

NGC	Type	Telescope	Atlas Page	Enlargement	Scale of Print sec/mm	NGC	Type	Telescope	Atlas Page	Enlargement	Scale of Print sec/mm
23	Sb	200″	22	16.0×	0.69	925	Sc/SBc	200″	37	2.5×	4.43
45	Sc	200″	37	2.0×	5.54	972	Sb	200″	23	6.0×	1.84
128	S0₁pec	200″	7	8.0×	1.38	Dwarf, 1023					
157	Sc	200″	29	9.4×	1.18	Group, I	Irr/Sc	200″	40	4.0×	2.76
175	SBa(s)	200″	43	7.0×	1.58	Dwarf, 1023					
185	E pec	200″	3	3.1×	3.57	Group, III	Irr/Sc	200″	40	4.1×	2.70
205	E pec/S0₁	200″	3	2.8×	3.94	1068	Sb	100″	16	8.0×	2.00
210	Sb	200″	22	4.0×	2.77	1073	SBc(sr)	200″	49	2.5×	4.42
224	Sb	48″	18	2.5×	25.7	1084	Sc	100″	29	7.1×	2.26
253	Sc	100″	34	3.0×	5.34	1087	Sc	60″	35	5.5×	4.94
309	Sc	200″	32	6.0×	1.84	1097	SBb(s)	100″	46	3.1×	5.16
404	S0₃	100″	6	16.8×	0.95	1156	Irr	200″	39	4.1×	2.70
488	Sb	200″	15	4.0×	2.76	1201	S0₁	200″	4	5.0×	2.21
520	Irr	200″	41	4.0×	2.76	1232	Sc	200″	32	2.0×	5.54
524	S0₂	200″	5	4.0×	2.76	1300	SBb(s)	200″	45	7.5×	1.47
598	Sc	48″	36	4.9×	13.6	1302	Sa	200″	9	3.5×	3.16
615	Sb	200″	22	7.0×	1.58	1398	SBb(r)	200″	47	4.0×	2.76
628	Sc	200″	29	1.7×	6.50	1637	Sc	200″	30	3.6×	3.08
628	Sc	200″	31	23.0×	0.48	1832	Sb	200″	21	5.0×	2.22
718	Sa	200″	11	8.2×	1.35	LMC	Irr	10″	38	1.6×	100.
750–751	E0/E0	200″	2	10.0×	1.11	1964	Sb	200″	22	4.0×	2.76
IC 1613	Irr	48″	40	6.0×	11.2	2217	SBa(r)	100″	43	4.2×	3.81
891	Sb	200″	25	1.2×	9.21	2217	SBa(r)	100″	43	4.2×	3.81
						2366	Irr	200″	39	2.2×	5.04
						2403	Sc	200″	36	2.0×	5.54

The Hubble Atlas

NGC	Type	Telescope	Atlas Page	Enlarge-ment	Scale of Print sec/mm	NGC	Type	Telescope	Atlas Page	Enlarge-ment	Scale of Print sec/mm
2523	SBb(r)	200″	48	6.0×	1.85	3145	Sb	100″	21	8.1×	1.98
2525	SBc(s)	100″	49	6.5×	2.46	3147	Sb	60″	20	8.2×	3.30
Ho II	Irr	200″	39	2.0×	5.54	3185	SBa(s)	200″	43	5.9×	1.88
2681	Sa	200″	9	4.1×	2.70	3245	S0$_1$	100″	4	9.0×	1.78
2685	S0 pec	200″	7	7.1×	1.56	IC 2574	Irr	200″	39	1.6×	6.91
2775	Sa	100″	10	9.2×	1.74	3329	S0$_1$	60″	4	19.2×	1.41
2811	Sa	200″	11	7.1×	1.56	3351	SBb(rs)	200″	48	3.0×	3.69
2841	Sb	200″	14	7.5×	1.48	3359	SBc(rs)	200″	49	3.0×	3.69
2855	S0$_3$/Sa(r)	200″	5	4.1×	2.70	3367	SBc(sr)	100″	49	8.1×	1.98
2859	SB0$_2$	200″	42	7.1×	1.56	3368	Sa	200″	12	6.0×	1.84
2903	Sc	200″	35	1.3×	8.50	3377	E6	200″	1	6.0×	1.84
2950	SB0$_{1/2}$	200″	42	2.2×	5.04	3504	SBb(s)/Sb	200″	46	5.9×	1.88
3031	Sb	200″	19	3.0×	3.69	3511	Sc	100″	35	3.5×	4.57
3032	S0$_3$	200″	5	10.0×	1.11	3521	Sb	100″	15	4.5×	3.56
3034	Irr	200″	41	3.0×	3.69	3556	Sc	60″	35	4.0×	6.78
3034	Irr	200″	41	3.0×	3.69	Leo II	E pec	200″	3	2.0×	5.54
3034	Irr	200″	41	3.0×	3.69	3623	Sa	100″	11	3.0×	5.34
3065	S0$_2$	200″	5	10.0×	1.11	3627	Sb	100″	23	7.2×	2.22
3077	Irr	200″	41	4.0×	2.76	3672	Sc	100″	30	5.0×	3.20
3081	Sa/SBa	100″	11	12.2×	1.31	3705	Sb	100″	21	4.0×	4.00
3109	Irr	60″	39	4.1×	6.61	3718	S0 pec?	60″	8	5.1×	5.32
3115	E7/S0$_1$	200″	1	4.1×	2.70	3810	Sc	100″	30	5.0×	3.20
Sextans System	Irr	200″	39	2.6×	4.25	3898	Sa	200″	10	6.0×	1.84
						4062	Sb	100″	20	4.1×	3.90

NGC	Type	Telescope	Atlas Page	Enlargement	Scale of Print sec/mm	NGC	Type	Telescope	Atlas Page	Enlargement	Scale of Print sec/mm
4088	SBc/Sc	60″	30	7.1×	3.82	4433	Sb	200″	23	9.0×	1.23
4111	S0$_2$	100″	6	8.2×	1.95	4449	Irr	100″	40	4.0×	4.00
4150	S0$_1$	100″	4	8.3×	1.93	4450	Sb	100″	13	4.0×	4.00
4214	Irr	200″	40	1.5×	7.38	4457	Sa	100″	9	11.9×	1.34
4215	S0$_2$	100″	6	10.0×	1.60	4459	S0$_3$	100″	5	19.2×	0.84
4216	Sb	100″	25	2.8×	5.72	4486	E0 pec	200″	2	7.0×	1.58
4237	Sb	100″	20	8.3×	1.93	4486	E0 pec	100″	2	15.0×	1.07
4244	Sc	200″	25	0.9×	12.3	4526	S0$_3$	60″	5	10.0×	2.71
4254	Sc	200″	29	2.8×	3.95	4548	SBb(sr)	200″	48	3.6×	3.08
4258	Sb	200″	33	5.5×	2.01	4565	Sb	200″	25	1.2×	9.23
4262	SB0$_{2/3}$	200″	42	7.1×	1.56	4569	Sb	200″	13	2.0×	5.54
4274	Sa	200″	12	3.5×	3.16	4579	Sb/SBb	200″	13	2.8×	3.96
4278	E1	200″	1	4.0×	2.76	4580	Sb	100″	21	12.1×	1.32
4293	Sa	100″	11	7.8×	2.05	4593	SBb(rs)	200″	48	4.0×	2.77
4303	Sc	200″	29	2.2×	5.04	4594	Sa/Sb	200″	24	6.6×	1.68
4314	SBa(s)pec	200″	44	8.0×	1.38	4612	SB0$_1$	200″	42	2.2×	5.04
4314	SBa(s)pec	100″	44	10.0×	1.60	4631	Sc	200″	25	1.0×	11.1
4321	Sc	100″	31	25.0×	0.64	4636	E0/S0$_1$	200″	1	6.0×	1.84
4321	Sc	200″	28	5.2×	2.12	4643	SB0$_3$/SBa(r)	200″	42	3.5×	3.16
4378	Sa	100″	10	5.2×	3.08	4656/7	Irr	60″	40	4.0×	6.78
4394	SBb(sr)	200″	47	6.2×	1.79	4684	S0$_1$	100″	4	7.1×	2.26
4395/4401	Sc/Irr	60″	37	3.5×	7.75	4691	Irr	200″	44	9.1×	1.22
4406	E3	200″	1	3.6×	3.08	4697	E5	200″	1	5.0×	2.22

NGC	Type	Telescope	Atlas Page	Enlarge-ment	Scale of Print sec/mm	NGC	Type	Telescope	Atlas Page	Enlarge-ment	Scale of Print sec/mm
4699	Sb	100″	16	6.0×	2.66	5364	Sc	200″	32	5.6×	1.98
4710	S0$_3$	100″	6	7.0×	2.28	5383	SBb(s)	60″	46	14.6×	1.86
4725	Sb/SBb	100″	21	2.2×	7.27	5457	Sc	200″	31	12.1×	0.92
4736	Sb	200″	16	3.2×	3.46	5457	Sc	200″	27	2.6×	4.25
4750	Sb	60″	21	22.2×	1.22	5566	SBa(r)	200″	43	3.0×	3.69
4753	S0 pec	100″	8	6.0×	2.67	5614	Sa	200″	9	6.2×	1.78
4762	S0$_1$	100″	8	8.8×	1.82	5866	S0$_3$	200″	6	3.0×	3.69
4793	Sc	100″	35	8.3×	1.93	5866	S0$_3$	200″	6	3.0×	3.69
4800	Sb	60″	16	19.2×	1.41	5907	Sc	200″	25	1.3×	8.52
4826	Sb	60″	13	3.7×	7.34	5962	Sc	100″	30	7.0×	2.29
4826	Sb	60″	13	3.7×	7.34	6181	Sc	100″	29	7.0×	2.29
4866	Sa	100″	11	6.1×	2.62	6384	Sb/SBb	100″	20	3.2×	5.00
4941	Sa/Sb	60″	10	10.2×	2.66	6643	Sc	60″	35	8.1×	3.35
5005	Sb	100″	13	3.6×	4.45	6814	Sb	200″	20	5.0×	2.22
5055	Sb	100″	15	3.6×	4.45	6951	SBb(s)/Sb	200″	46	5.0×	2.22
5101	SB0$_3$/SBa(s)	200″	42	4.5×	2.46	7217	Sb	200″	15	4.0×	2.76
5128	(E0 + Sb)?	200″	50	3.5×	3.16	7314	Sc	200″	30	3.0×	3.69
5194	Sc	100″	31	16.0×	1.00	7331	Sb	200″	17	5.1×	2.17
5194/5	Sc/Irr	200″	26	4.8×	2.30	7332	S0$_2$ pec	200″	7	5.0×	2.22
5195	Irr	200″	26	4.8×	2.30	7392	Sb	100″	20	8.0×	2.00
5204	Sc/Irr	200″	37	6.2×	1.79	7457	S0$_1$	100″	4	5.9×	2.72
5236	Sc/SBb	100″	28	3.3×	4.85	7640	SBc(s)	200″	49	1.2×	9.22
5248	Sc	200″	33	5.0×	2.22	7741	SBc(s)	200″	49	4.1×	2.70
5273	S0$_2$/Sa(s)	200″	8	6.0×	1.85	7743	SBa(s)	200″	43	6.5×	1.70

Illustrations of Galaxies

NGC 4636   E0/S0₁
PH–371–B
May 4/5, 1951
103aO + GG1
30 min
Enlarged 6.0×

The central isophotes of NGC 4636 appear circular on short-exposure plates. On these plates, and on the illustration on the right, this galaxy looks like a normal E0. On plates taken with the 48-inch Schmidt telescope, however, a faint elliptical envelope appears whose major axis is at a position angle of 330° (north through east). The ellipticity of the envelope is E4. Its surface brightness is about 24 mag/sq sec. Because of the envelope, this galaxy must be considered a transition to S0₁ type.

There are many condensations in the atmosphere of NGC 4636 that can be seen on this illustration. They are probably globular clusters of about $M_{pg} = -10.0$.

NGC 4697   E5
PH–374–B
May 5/6, 1951
103aO + GG1
30 min
Enlarged 5.0×

NGC 4697 is a normal E5 galaxy in the southern extension of the Virgo Cluster. There are a number of condensations whose distribution is centered on the nucleus; they are probably globular clusters. If this galaxy has a modulus of $m - M = 30.7$, which probably applies to the nucleus of the Virgo Cluster, then M_{pg} for NGC 4697 is -20.3. The value $m_{pg} = 10.4$ is from Humason et al. (*A. J.*, *61*, 97, 1956, table A1).

NGC 4278   E1
PH–676–S
Feb. 7/8, 1954
103aD + GG11
45 min
Enlarged 4.0×

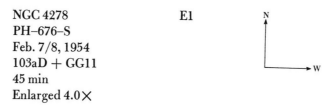

NGC 4278 is a typical E1 galaxy. There is a smooth intensity gradient from the center to the outside where the luminosity of the galaxy fades far below the surface brightness of the background sky. There is no outer envelope like that in S0₁ systems.

The many condensations in the atmosphere of 4278 are undoubtedly globular clusters. There are not so many of them here as in 4486 (M87), but about 50 exist. NGC 4278 is north of the Virgo Cluster, in the south wing of the Ursa Major Cloud.

NGC 3377   E6
PH–53–S
Nov. 29/30, 1951
103aO + WG2
30 min
Enlarged 6.0×

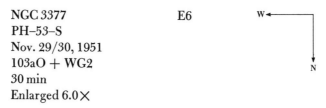

NGC 3377 is a normal E6 galaxy in a small physical group whose members include 3351 (M95), 3368 (M96), 3379, 3384, 3412, 3489. The redshift of the group averages about 650 km/sec. It is close to, and probably a dynamical unit of, the larger group in Leo whose brightest members are NGC 3627, 3623, etc. (See table XI of Humason et al., *A. J.*, *61*, 97, 1956.)

NGC 4406   M86   E3
PH–39–B
Apr. 20/21, 1950
103aO
30 min
Enlarged 3.6×

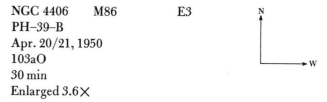

NGC 4406 is a normal E3 galaxy. The luminosity gradient is uniform. There is no evidence of an external envelope as in NGC 4636 or in normal S0₁ galaxies. NGC 4406 is a giant E galaxy, in the Virgo Cluster, of $M_{pg} = -20.6$ and $m_{pg} = 10.1$ (Holmberg, *Medd. Lunds Astr. Obs.*, ser. II, no. 136, 1958). The distance modulus is $m - M = 30.7$.

NGC 3115   E7/S0₁
PH–20–Bm
Mar. 30/31, 1952
103aE + E.K. no. 25
60 min
Enlarged 4.1×

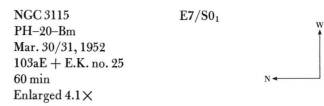

NGC 3115 was classified as a true E7 on the basis of plates taken with the 60- and the 100-inch telescopes. Plates taken with the 200-inch clearly show two subsystems: one an almost spherical nuclear system; and the second, a thin fundamental plane. The plane was detected in the photometry of Hubble (*Ap. J.*, *71*, 231, 1930) and of Oort (*Ap. J.*, *91*, 273, 1940). NGC 3115 is now classed as either a transition between E7 and S0₁ or a pure S0₁.

1

2

NGC 4486   M87   E0 pec   W ←┐
PH–422–MH   │
Apr. 15/16, 1952   ↓ N
103aO
30 min
Enlarged 7.0×

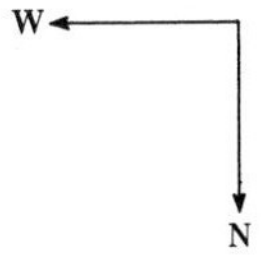

NGC 4486 (M87) is the brightest elliptical galaxy in the Virgo Cluster. The apparent photographic magnitude is about $m_{pg} = 9.7$ (mean of Holmberg and Pettit-Sandage). If $m - M = 30.7$ for the Virgo Cluster, then $M_{pg} = -21.0$ for 4486. This is one of the brightest galaxies known. M31 has $M_{pg} = -20.3$; NGC 128 has $M_{pg} = -21.5$; and a few others are as bright. There is no question that NGC 4486 is on the bright end of the luminosity function.

NGC 4486 is peculiar in two respects. First, a very large number (well over 500) of globular clusters are scattered over the entire image; they show quite well in the outer regions of the illustration. Second, a peculiar jet starts from the nucleus and can be traced for 1500 parsecs in the northwest direction. It is visible on the illustration on the upper right of the facing page.

This galaxy is a source of intense radio emission. The relation of the optical image to the radio source is discussed by Baade and Minkowski in *Ap. J.*, *119*, 221, 1954.

NGC 4486   M87   E0 pec   W ←┐
H–1607–H   │
Mar. 8/9, 1934   ↓ N
E40
15 min
Enlarged 15.0×

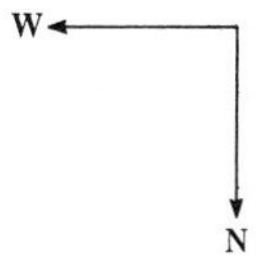

The jet in NGC 4486 is well shown in this illustration. The orientation is the same as that of the illustration on the left. The light of the two knots in the jet is polarized. An illustrated discussion of the polarization is given by Baade (*Ap. J.*, *123*, 550, 1956).

NGC 750/751   E0/E0   W
PH–774–S   │
Aug. 23/24, 1954   N ←───┘
103aD + GG11
25 min
Enlarged 10.0×

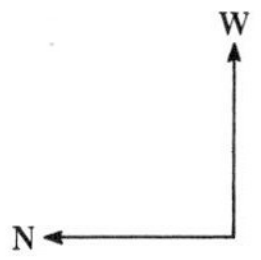

NGC 750/751 form a double galaxy of two normal E0 systems. The two components are connected by a luminous bridge. An extensive outer envelope surrounds the two nuclei.

NGC 185   E pec
PH–648–B
Aug. 21/22, 1952
103aD + GG11
60 min
Enlarged 3.1×

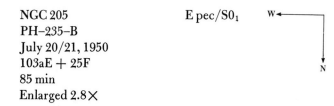

The three galaxies shown on the facing page illustrate the resolution of elliptical galaxies into stars. All three are members of the Local Group. The resolution of NGC 185 and NGC 205 was first accomplished by Baade with the 100-inch telescope (*Ap. J.*, *100*, 137–150, 1944). The photographs here of 185 and 205 were taken by Baade with the 200-inch.

NGC 185 and NGC 147 together with M31, M32, and NGC 205 form a subunit of the Local Group. All five have distance moduli of about $m - M = 24.4$ to 24.6.

A dust patch near the center of 185 is more easily seen on a photograph by Baade reproduced in the reference cited.

Leo II System (Sculptor Type) E
PH–904–S
Mar. 24/25, 1955
103aD + GG11
45 min
Enlarged 2.0×

The Leo II system is classed as a dwarf elliptical. The galaxy is within the Local Group and is highly resolved into stars. There is no background surface luminosity as in normal E galaxies, because the stellar content is so sparse. This galaxy is similar to the Sculptor and Fornax systems discovered in 1938 at Harvard (see Baade and Hubble, *Pubs. A. S. P.*, *51*, 40, 1936). Leo II, together with three similar systems, was discovered on the Palomar Sky Survey by Harrington and Wilson (A. G. Wilson, *Pubs. A. S. P.*, *67*, 27, 1955). Many RR Lyrae stars have been found in Leo II. The distance modulus is about $m - M = 21.8$. The color-magnitude diagram of the Draco system, which is similar to that of Leo II, is almost identical to that of a typical globular cluster.

NGC 205   E pec/S0₁
PH–235–B
July 20/21, 1950
103aE + 25F
85 min
Enlarged 2.8×

NGC 205 is one of the two elliptical companions of M31. Note how the outer parts of 205 are highly resolved into stars on this 200-inch plate. The brightest of these stars are all of about the same apparent brightness. This explains the observational fact that resolution does not occur until a critical exposure time is reached, at which time the entire smooth image of the galaxy breaks up into individual stars.

NGC 205 has two features uncommon to pure elliptical systems. (1) There are two dust patches near the center of the galaxy. They are not completely opaque. They do not show in this illustration because of the high stellar density near the center, but a negative reproduction of a good 100-inch plate taken by Hubble and published in *Sky and Telescope*, January 1954, does show the feature. (2) A few blue supergiant stars appear to be associated with dust patches in the center of NGC 205. A negative print from an ultraviolet plate taken by Baade with the 100-inch is given in *Pub. Michigan Obs.*, *10*, 10.

The intensity gradient of NGC 205 suggests the presence of an outer envelope similar to that of S0₁ galaxies. Perhaps this is a transition case.

3

4

NGC 1201   S0₁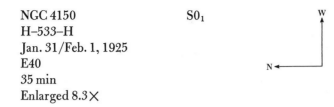
PH–817–S
Oct. 1/2, 1954
103aO
25 min
Enlarged 5.0×

NGC 4150   S0₁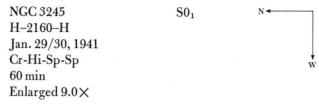
H–533–H
Jan. 31/Feb. 1, 1925
E40
35 min
Enlarged 8.3×

NGC 3245   S0₁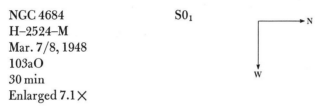
H–2160–H
Jan. 29/30, 1941
Cr-Hi-Sp-Sp
60 min
Enlarged 9.0×

The six galaxies on the facing page are all classic examples of $S0_1$. The image of each is smooth, with no evidence of dust. The galaxies differ from E systems in the luminosity gradients. A faint, extensive envelope is present in all $S0_1$ galaxies. As this feature does not show well in halftone reproductions it may be partly lost in these illustrations.

To the eye, images of $S0_1$ present three distinct luminosity zones on the original plate. There is an intense nucleus, an intermediate zone of lower surface brightness, called the lens, and the characteristic faint outer envelope. This description may be subjective. The luminosity gradients may be continuous, and the three zones may be a photographic effect. The effect does, however, provide criteria for classification.

The three zones mentioned in the description of 1201 are well marked here. The outer envelope of 4150 is very extensive. This places 4150 later in the $S0_1$ classification than NGC 1201. Microphotometer tracings should be made of these galaxies to find the real difference in the luminosity gradients of E and $S0_1$ galaxies. At present the classification depends entirely on subjective impressions gained from visual inspection of photographic plates.

NGC 3245 is one of the best examples of $S0_1$ shown on the page. The outer envelope is quite extensive. It is often difficult to classify a galaxy which is near the E or $S0_1$ boundary. NGC 3245 is a "late" $S0_1$, and there is no difficulty of classification.

The original plate of 3245 shows that the nucleus is spherical and the lens and outer envelope are elliptical.

NGC 4684   S0₁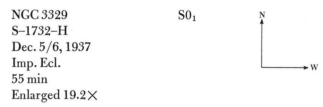
H–2524–M
Mar. 7/8, 1948
103aO
30 min
Enlarged 7.1×

This and 3329 are good type examples of $S0_1$ galaxies. The three characteristic zones of different luminosity are present.

NGC 3329   S0₁   N
S–1732–H
Dec. 5/6, 1937
Imp. Ecl.
55 min
Enlarged 19.2×

The description of this galaxy is the same as for the other five systems shown.

NGC 7457   S0₁   N
H–2550–H
Dec. 1/2, 1948
103aO
30 min
Enlarged 5.9×

This is a good example of a typical $S0_1$. The galaxy is so similar to the other $S0_1$ systems shown on the page that no individual description is necessary.

NGC 524   SO₂
PH–829–S
Oct. 2/3, 1954
103aD + GG11
45 min
Enlarged 4.0✕

NGC 524 shows a pattern of nucleus, lens, and envelope. The lens, on visual inspection of the photographs, appears to be surrounded by a relatively dark zone, followed by a more luminous zone. This description is subjective, however. Microphotometer tracings show that the luminosity decreases continuously outward from the nucleus. The apparent dark zone corresponds to a region where the rate of fall first increases then slows and finally approximates the normal value. (NGC 3065 is similar to 524. The description follows below.)

NGC 3065   SO₂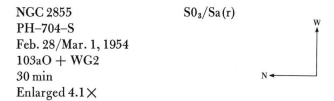
PH–866–S
Nov. 3/4, 1954
103aO
20 min
Enlarged 10.0✕

The form of the luminosity curve might be accounted for either by a circular ring of partial obscuration in the middle of the envelope or by a concentration of luminosity near the boundary. In either event, a segregation of material is indicated. This illustration of 3065 is very poor; nothing but the nucleus and lens shows. The subjective $I(r)$ curve for this galaxy is shown in the drawing below.

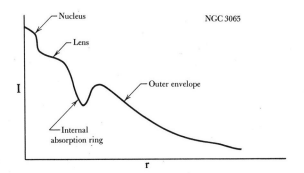

NGC 3032   SO₃
PH–853–S
Nov. 2/3, 1954
103aO
30 min
Enlarged 10.0✕

NGC 3032 and NGC 4459 (right) are excellent type examples of SO₃ systems. The internal "absorption ring" of 3065 (shown in the subjective $I(r)$ curve in the lower left) has deepened to almost zero intensity and appears as a complete internal ring. The absorption ring is embedded in the lens. A very faint envelope is present, but it is not shown on the reproduction. Regions of faint luminosity are almost impossible to reproduce on paper prints; this difficulty is evident throughout the atlas.

NGC 2855   SO₃/Sa(r)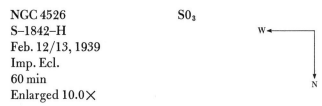
PH–704–S
Feb. 28/Mar. 1, 1954
103aO + WG2
30 min
Enlarged 4.1✕

On 100-inch plates, NGC 2855 appeared to have a central absorption ring like 3032 and 4459. However, this reproduction from a 200-inch plate shows that the ring in 2855 has definite spiral structure, winding in a very tight pattern into the outer envelope. The spiral arms are defined completely by the dust lanes winding out through a luminous background. The dust lanes are so nearly circular that NGC 2855 is considered to be a transition case from SO₃ to Sa(r).

NGC 4459   SO₃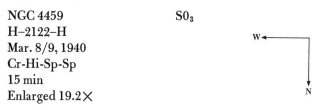
H–2122–H
Mar. 8/9, 1940
Cr-Hi-Sp-Sp
15 min
Enlarged 19.2✕

The form of NGC 4459 is nearly identical to that of 3032 (left) except that the internal absorption ring is more regular. The ring can be traced through an entire revolution, although it is less opaque on the south side. This may be a projection effect where the bright central nucleus is spherical and projects in front of the far side of the absorption lane.

NGC 4526   SO₃
S–1842–H
Feb. 12/13, 1939
Imp. Ecl.
60 min
Enlarged 10.0✕

NGC 4526 is a good example of an SO₃ seen at a large projection angle. The internal ring is blocked on the far side by the spherical nucleus projecting in front of the ring. A very large outer envelope, characteristic of SO₁, can be traced on the original negative for a distance of 230 sec of arc, which corresponds to 85 mm on this illustration.

5

6

NGC 404   SO₃
H–2115–H
Oct. 13/14, 1939
103aO
55 min
Enlarged 16.8×

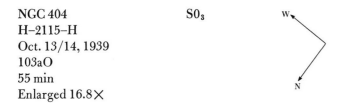

In many respects NGC 404 appears to be a normal SO₃ with a circular dust lane embedded in a uniform lens and envelope. The lane cannot be traced through a complete revolution. Although this might be explained as a projection effect similar to that of NGC 4459 and NGC 4526 on page 5, the explanation is probably inadequate because the background envelope of 404 (not visible in the illustration) is elliptical. Therefore the fundamental plane of the galaxy is not perpendicular to the line of sight. But the absorption ring is placed along the minor axis of the ellipse. It would have to be along the major axis if the orientation explanation for its incompleteness is correct.

NGC 4111   SO₂
H–1751–H
May 24/25, 1936
Imp. Ecl.
15 min
Enlarged 8.2×

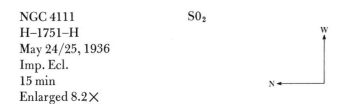

NGC 4111 is classified as an SO₂ seen on edge. The nucleus, lens, and outer envelope are all easily visible on the original plate and can probably be made out in this illustration. The surface brightness of the lens is not uniform, but two absorbing streaks appear, in projection, perpendicular to the fundamental plane. They cross the lens near its junction with the nucleus. Such a pattern would be reproduced if NGC 3065 were seen on edge. The internal absorption lane of the galaxy would then appear silhouetted against the bright background.

NGC 4710   SO₃
H–2483–H
Jan. 9/10, 1948
IIaO
5 min
Enlarged 7.0×

The unusual feature of an internal absorption band and bright ansae on the central lens would be produced if NGC 3032 (p. 5) or NGC 4459 (p. 5) were seen on edge. Consequently, NGC 4710 is classified as an SO₃ on edge. A faint outer envelope can be traced to 160 sec from the nucleus, corresponding to 70 mm on the illustration.

NGC 5866   SO₃
PH–721–S
Apr. 6/7, 1954
103aO + WG2
15 min
Enlarged 3.0×

Two views of NGC 5866 are given. This short exposure shows the internal dust lane, which is similar to that of NGC 4710 above.

Note the tilt of the dust by about 2° to the plane defined by the bright ansae and the elliptical halo. The second view of NGC 5866, from a long-exposure plate, is shown on the right.

NGC 4215   SO₂
H–771–H
May 24/25, 1927
E40
40 min
Enlarged 10.0×

NGC 4215 has a bright nucleus and an extended lens. The intensity distribution of the lens is not uniform. There is evidence of internal absorption such as would be produced if NGC 3065 (p. 5) or a less dense central ring version of 3032 (p. 5) were to be seen on edge. The absorption across the lens of 4215 occurs as two hazy vertical bands internal to the edge of the galaxy. The ends of the image are bright as in NGC 4710. This would be the case if 3065 were tipped on edge, because no absorption would reach the outside edges.

NGC 5866   SO₃
PH–195–MH
May 13/14, 1950
103aO
30 min
Enlarged 3.0×

The dust lane of NGC 5866 does not appear in this illustration. The fact that the image looks like a regular E6 galaxy with no abnormality shows the danger of missing faint but important details on plates taken with small-scale telescopes or with long exposures.

NGC 128 SO_1pec
PH–771–S
Aug. 23/24, 1954
103aD + GG11
30 min
Enlarged 8.0×

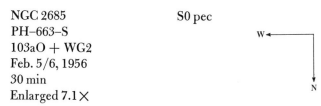

NGC 128 has a peculiar box-shaped nucleus. Otherwise, it resembles a normal SO_1 on edge. There is no evidence for absorbing rings perpendicular to the plane such as could explain the indentation of the center of the nucleus. The box-shaped nucleus must therefore be a dynamical feature of the galaxy.

    NGC 128 is the brightest member of a group. The two other galaxies appearing with it in this illustration are NGC 127 north preceding and NGC 130 north following 128. Both are dynamical members of the group and are at the same distance as 128. In a luminous bridge between NGC 127 and 128, absorption lanes are seen silhouetted against the north ansa of 128.

NGC 7332 SO_2pec
PH–768–S
Aug. 23/24, 1954
103aO
30 min
Enlarged 5.0×

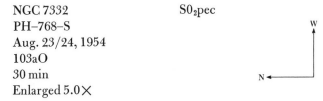

Short exposures of NGC 7332 show that this galaxy is similar to NGC 4111 and NGC 4215. Absorption lanes, in projection, appear as narrow bands perpendicular to the fundamental plane. These bands are probably the ends of the internal ring of SO_2 galaxies, like 3065, seen in projection against the lens. NGC 7332 is classed as peculiar because of the box-shaped central region, in which feature it is similar to NGC 128. Otherwise NGC 7332 appears to be normal.

NGC 2685 SO pec
PH–663–S
103aO + WG2
Feb. 5/6, 1956
30 min
Enlarged 7.1×

NGC 2685 is perhaps the most unusual galaxy in the Shapley-Ames catalogue. There are two axes of symmetry for the projected image; most galaxies have only one. The central, amorphous spindle resembles a normal SO_1 seen on edge. However, helical filaments surround the spindle. Because of projection effects, it is impossible to tell whether these filaments form complete circles around the spindle or whether they start somewhere on the spindle and spiral outward at right angles to its axis. The filaments are seen in absorption when they pass in front of the bright background, but they are luminous when they are not silhouetted. Note how the entire northeast end of the spindle is covered with the projected absorption lanes of the helix.

    A luminous external ring around the entire structure may be either a true ring or a complete shell seen in projection.

    Many questions are unanswered about this galaxy. Is the central feature a spheroid (with two axes equal as in a plate or pancake), or is it an ellipsoid like a cigar? What is the direction of the angular momentum vector? Is the external ring attached to the central regions, or is it separate?

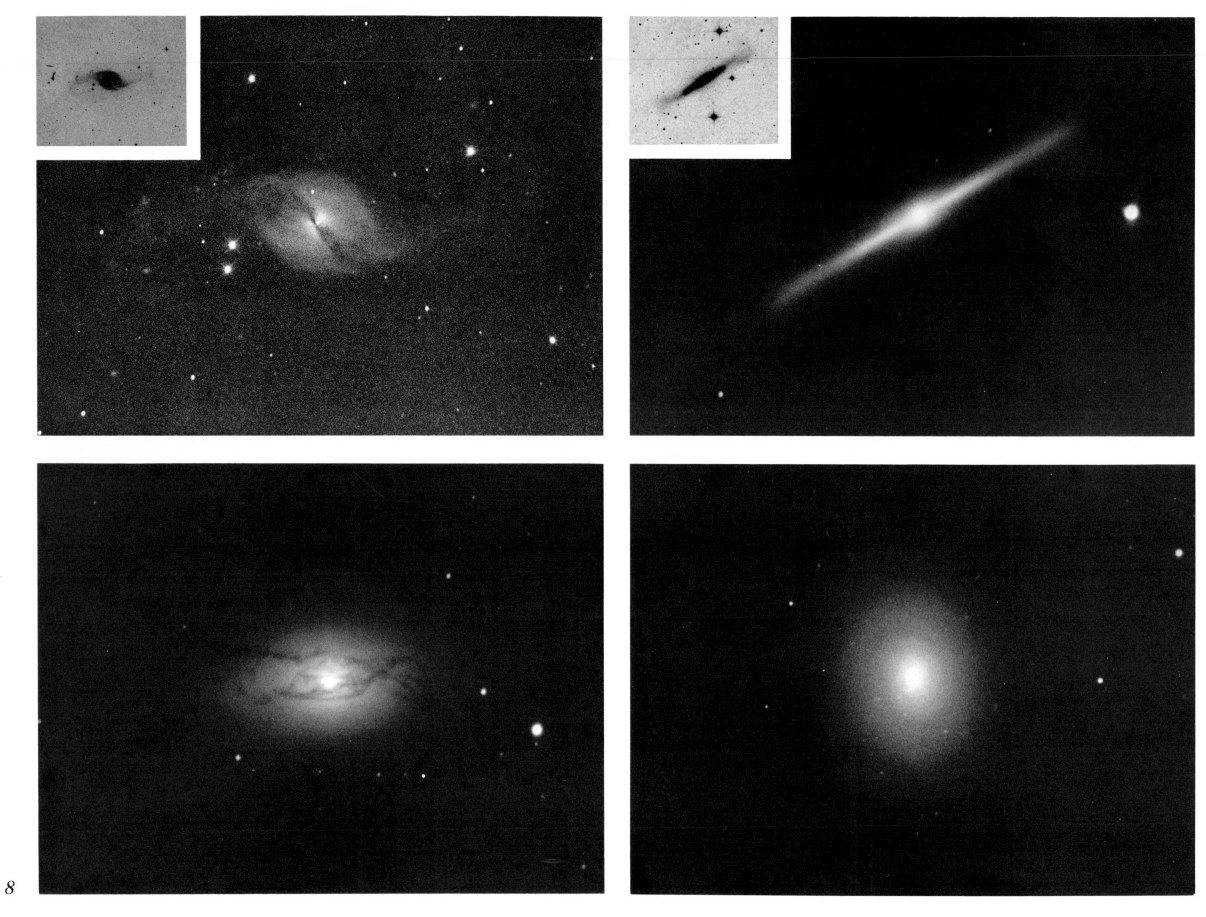

8

NGC 3718   S0 pec?
S–1802–H
May 23/24, 1938
Agfa Blue
120 min
Enlarged 5.1×

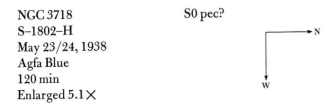

NGC 3718 and NGC 4753 (below) were classified by Hubble as S0 pec because, if the unusual absorption features were removed, the underlying luminosity would resemble $S0_1$ galaxies. But, at least for NGC 3718, the form is not this simple. Two faint extensions to the envelope emerge from opposite sides of the periphery in NGC 3718. They suggest spiral arms. This galaxy looks somewhat like an SBb but the absorption lane *is* the bar. But the bars of all *normal* SB galaxies are luminous, bright features and are not absorption bands. The modern data, therefore, place NGC 3718 outside the sequence of classification. The insert photograph is from the 48-inch Schmidt.

NGC 4753   S0 pec
H–2502–H
Feb. 8/9, 1948
103aO
30 min
Enlarged 6.0×

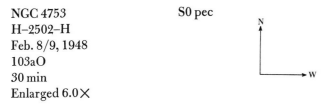

NGC 4753 was classified by Hubble as S0 pec because, if the many irregular absorption lanes were removed, the underlying luminosity distribution would resemble an $S0_1$.

NGC 4762 $S0_1$
H–282–H
Apr. 15/16, 1923
S30
135 min
Enlarged 8.8×

NGC 4762 has the flattest form of any galaxy known. It is undoubtedly an $S0_1$ seen on edge. The nucleus, lens, and extended envelope are all visible on the original plate and probably show in this illustration. Note the very faint outer extensions visible on the insert photograph. This insert was made from a 48-inch Schmidt plate.

NGC 5273 $S0_2$/Sa(s)
PH–668–S
Feb. 5/6, 1954
103aO + WG2
30 min
Enlarged 6.0×

NGC 5273 is a transition between an $S0_2$ and an Sa galaxy. A very faint spiral pattern is visible. It is probably due to a thin dust lane that winds outward through the envelope. The lane is not opaque, so that the arms are difficult to trace.

NGC 2681   Sa
PH–191–MH
May 13/14, 1950
103aO
30 min
Enlarged 4.1×

NGC 2681 and NGC 1302 (right) are the earliest Sa galaxies shown in the atlas. NGC 2681 has two well defined
spiral arms in its central region. These arms, shown in
the insert, are very tightly wound about the nucleus. It
is probable that the region between the stubby arms and
the intense nucleus is filled with dust.

There is a faint and very poorly defined outer spiral
structure. The direction of unwinding of the spiral pattern is almost impossible to trace. NGC 2681 is discussed
by Lindblad and Brahde in *Ap. J.*, *104*, 211, 1946; they
give several pictures of the galaxy.

NGC 4457   Sa
H–2481–H
Jan. 9/10, 1948
103aO
30 min
Enlarged 11.9×

NGC 4457 has one prominent spiral arm of high surface
brightness, and another, fainter arm which is less well defined. These arms are embedded in an envelope of low
surface brightness. Dust lanes lie on the insides of the
two arms. A faint external ring surrounds the entire
structure. The ring may not be completely detached from
the more central envelope, because a faint connection is
probably present on the east end of the major axis.

NGC 1302   Sa
PH–670–S
Feb. 6/7, 1954
103aD + GG11
45 min
Enlarged 3.5×

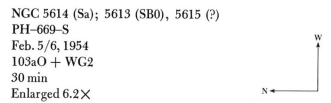

NGC 1302 is similar to 2681. The inner arms near the
nucleus of 1302 are more difficult to trace than those in
2681, but the outer pattern is slightly better defined. It is
not known whether the outer structure is due to thin dust
lanes winding out through a smooth envelope or to an
actual spiral distribution of luminous matter. In any case,
the spiral pattern is almost circular; the arms are very
diffuse and hard to trace.

NGC 5614 (Sa); 5613 (SB0), 5615 (?)
PH–669–S
Feb. 5/6, 1954
103aO + WG2
30 min
Enlarged 6.2×

Three galaxies are shown in this illustration. The large
one is NGC 5614, which is classified as Sa. The knot on
the northwest rim of 5614 is called NGC 5615; it may be a
separate galaxy in collision with 5614, but the interpretation is uncertain. The SB0 on the left side of the print is
NGC 5613. Note its beautiful external ring.

The spiral pattern in NGC 5614 is composed both of
tightly wound luminous filaments and interspersed dust
lanes. The arms are almost circular. Hence, NGC 5614
is classified as early Sa.

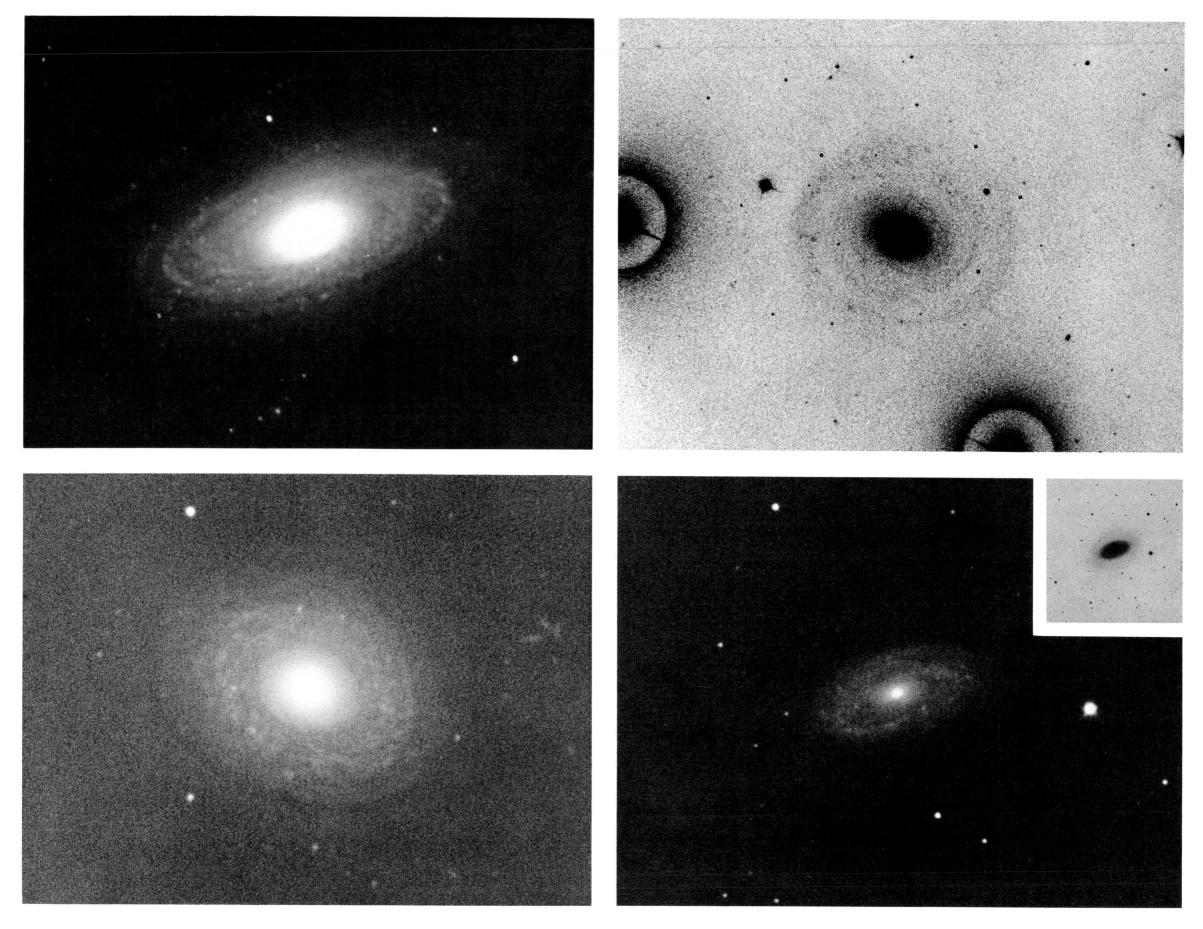

NGC 3898   Sa
PH–909–S
Mar. 25/26, 1955
103aO + WG2
30 min
Enlarged 6.0×

NGC 3898 is the Sa prototype of multiple-arm spirals of the NGC 2841 [Sb, p. *14*] type. The arms in 3898 are very tightly wound about a large amorphous center. The arms themselves are made up of individual segments which cannot be traced as complete arcs for more than 20° to 30°. NGC 3898 is one of the earliest members of a sequence of multiple-arm spirals which can be traced from late Sc to early Sa. Among the members of this sequence are M101 (p. *27*), NGC 5055 (p. *15*), 488 (p. *15*), 2841 (p. *14*), 3898 (this galaxy), 2811 (p. *11*), and 1302 (p. *9*).

NGC 2775   Sa
H–2064–H
Mar. 24/25, 1939
Agfa Blue
80 min
Enlarged 9.2×

This beautiful spiral is similar to NGC 3898. The spiral pattern is more easily seen because NGC 2775 is observed almost face on. Notice that the arms cannot be traced as individual structures but rather as separate segments, as is true in all multiple-arm galaxies of types Sa and Sb. The arms, with their associated dust lanes, start abruptly at the edge of a completely amorphous central nucleus and lens. The boundary between the lens and the spiral structure is sharp.

Note the thin dust lane on the outside of the entire pattern (about 45 mm from the center on this illustration, along the major axis).

NGC 4378   Sa
H–2482–H
Jan. 9/10, 1948
103aO
30 min
Enlarged 5.2×

The spiral pattern in this galaxy is formed either by thin dust lanes threading outward through a uniform envelope or by luminous filaments. The surface brightness of the envelope or the filaments is exceedingly small. It probably averages about 22 mag/sq sec of arc, which is close to the brightness of the night sky. The original plate was triple-printed to bring up the contrast: i.e., a positive contact plate was made from the original negative; a copy negative was made from this positive; a second contact positive was made from the copy negative; and the photographic print was made from this last plate. The illustration is very grainy because of the process.

NGC 4941   Sa/Sb
S–1655–H
May 4/5, 1937
Imp. Ecl.
50 min
Enlarged 10.2×

This galaxy is difficult to classify because of conflicting criteria. The spiral arms are tightly wound. There are only two arms, and they overlap after each has turned through 180°. There is little or no dust in the arms, which are relatively smooth textured with not much resolution into lumps or H II knots. The arms therefore suggest a classification of Sa. The nucleus is very small, however, suggesting a classification of Sb or even Sc. This galaxy shows that the three classification criteria are not always consistent.

NGC 4293   Sa
H–772–H
May 24/25, 1927
E40
60 min
Enlarged 7.8×

All galaxies on the facing page are in the second major subdivision of Sa systems. They all have predominantly small nuclei, more or less regular, thin, internal dust lanes, and thin spiral arms. The earliest galaxy of the group is NGC 2811; the latest is NGC 3623. NGC 4293 has heavy absorption lanes spread throughout the lens. This galaxy may be the Sa example of the NGC 253 (p. *34*) type of Sc spirals.

NGC 2811   Sa
PH–703–S
Feb. 28/Mar. 1, 1954
103aO + WG2
30 min
Enlarged 7.1×

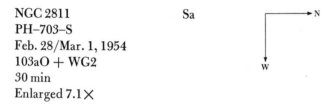

NGC 2811 is one of the earliest Sa galaxies shown in the atlas. Notice the central nucleus embedded in an amorphous lens. Smooth, thin, tightly wound spiral arms start at the edge of the lens. They suggest a multiple-arm pattern like that of NGC 2841 (Sb, p. *14*), but the pattern is much tighter and less well defined here. There is no trace of resolution. The photographic image of all parts of this galaxy is smooth.

NGC 4866   Sa
H–377–H
July 3/4, 1924
S30
60 min
Enlarged 6.1×

NGC 4866 is the prototype galaxy of the second major subgroup of Sa systems. Very thin dust lanes are spread throughout the main body. They are not circular but have a tightly wound spiral pattern. NGC 4866 and 2811 probably have a similar spiral pattern, but the projection angles differ in the two galaxies. Notice the small nucleus to NGC 4866. The entire lens is amorphous with no suggestion of resolution into stars.

NGC 3623   M65   Sa
H–494–H
Nov. 26/27, 1924
S30
75 min
Enlarged 3.0×

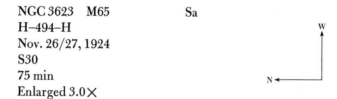

NGC 3623 is the latest Sa shown in the atlas. In an older notation it would have been called Sab. Note the prominent dust lane silhouetted against the bright background. There is no resolution of the arms into knots, but the photographic image of the lens and arms is not as smooth as for 4866 or 718. A negative reproduction of NGC 3623 is given by Hubble in *Ap. J.*, *97*, 112, 1943.

NGC 718   Sa
PH–792–S
Aug. 25/26, 1954
103aO + WG2
30 min
Enlarged 8.2×

NGC 718 has three sets of spiral arms. The inner set is very tightly coiled about a small nucleus. The nucleus looks large here, but this photographic effect in the reproduction process is due to the coalescence of the inner, tightly wound arms. The second set of arms can be seen close to the burned-out nuclear region. The arm on the northwest side is most easily visible. Finally, two very faint arms sweep far from the nucleus. There is no trace of resolution into stars over the entire galaxy.

NGC 3081   Sa/SBa
H–2478–H
Jan. 9/10, 1948
103aO
30 min
Enlarged 12.2×

NGC 3081 has two spiral arms which nearly overlap each other, giving the impression of a complete external ring separate from the nucleus. Close inspection of the photograph, however, shows the two separate arms to be very tightly wound. The form is similar to that of NGC 3185, the description of whose arms on page *43* should be read. NGC 3081 differs from 3185 in lacking an intense bar connecting the ends of the broken ring. On long-exposure plates a faint bar can be traced in 3081, but its faintness puts the galaxy in the Sa rather than in the SBa class.

11

12

NGC 4274   Sa
PH–686–S
Feb. 9/10, 1954
103aO + WG2
30 min
Enlarged 3.5×

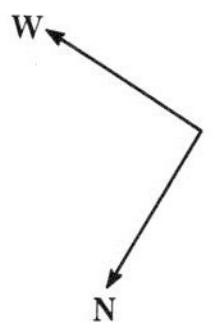

NGC 3368   M96   Sa
PH–869–S
Nov. 3/4, 1954
103aO
20 min
Enlarged 6.0×

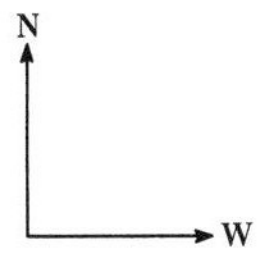

NGC 4274 is the type example of a special subgroup of Sa within the NGC 4866 major group. On short-exposure photographs, all galaxies of this subgroup appear to have a complete narrow ring, separated from the nucleus, and superposed on the faint background light of the lens. Large-scale photographs, however, show that the ring is *not* complete but is broken at diametrically opposite places, the pieces having drifted outward to form a spiral pattern.

This feature is particularly well shown in NGC 4274. The two bright spiral arms that make up the broken ring are easily visible. Notice how the two arms almost touch when the one sweeps through 180° and passes near the arm closer to the nucleus.

Two fainter arms are present in NGC 4274, winding outward through an extended envelope on the outside of the bright arms that form the "broken ring."

NGC 3368 is of the NGC 4274 (left) type but is later along the sequence of classification. Remnants of the "broken ring" are visible in the two arms which begin in the nucleus and circle the rim of the lens. NGC 3368 is seen more nearly face-on than NGC 4274, and so the arms do not appear to overlap as much as in 4274.

Very faint filaments, circling the entire inner structure, are visible in the insert. They are connected to the inner lens near the northwest end of the major axis.

NGC 4826   M64   Sb
Ri–65 (60″)
May 5, 6, 7, 8, 1910
7 hr 56 min
Enlarged 3.7×

NGC 4569   M90   Sb
PH–12–Bm
Jan. 31/Feb. 1, 1952
103aO + WG2
30 min
Enlarged 2.0×

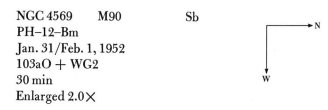

NGC 4450   Sb
H–2432–H
May 17/18, 1947
103aO
25 min
Enlarged 4.0×

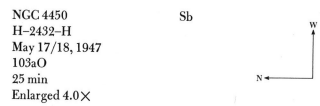

NGC 4826 is the earliest Sb shown in the atlas. This plate was taken by Ritchey in a four-night exposure with the 60-inch. Note the very soft texture to the spiral arms. These arms are nearly circular, and they show no trace of resolution into knots. NGC 4826 is classed as Sb rather than as Sa because of the very heavy dust lane in the center, which is shown below.

NGC 4826   M64   Sb
Ri–58 (60″)
Mar. 8/9, 1910
240 min
Enlarged 3.7×

This is a shorter exposure of NGC 4826 than the one shown above. The dust pattern in the nucleus is very prominent. The bright filaments, which make up the inner spiral structure, are also visible. Although the strongest concentration of the dust is in a single dark lane, a fainter dust arm can be seen on the inner edge of the last luminous arm on the north side of the galaxy in this illustration.

The soft texture of the spiral arms and the heavy dust lanes near the center of this galaxy are similar to these features in 4826 (left). Spiral arms of this type were described as "massive" by Reynolds and by Hubble. Dust lanes can be traced almost to the nucleus, which is of high surface brightness and about 2 mm in diameter on the scale of this illustration. There is partial resolution of one of the inner dust lanes into knots, which are presumed to be H II regions.

NGC 4579   M58   Sb/SBb
PH–28–Bm
Mar. 31/Apr. 1, 1952
103aO + WG2
30 min
Enlarged 2.8×

This galaxy is a much later example of the 4569 subgroup than 4826 or 4569 itself. There are two very faint outer spiral arms which are smooth in texture and are "massive" in the sense of the spiral arms in 4826 and 4569. They do not show well in the illustration because of their low surface brightness. Two thin dust lanes can be traced in this outer region near the smooth, massive arm, on the north side of the galaxy. More prominent dust lanes, thin and well defined, can be traced on the inside of the bright inner spiral arms. There is a bar of enhanced luminosity across the central amorphous region, though it is not well enough defined to classify NGC 4579 as an SBb. The galaxy is a transition between Sb and SBb. Note the partial resolution of the arms into knots.

This galaxy is an intermediate case of the 4826 group. The plate was taken with the 100-inch after the war, when the city lights from Los Angeles were bright. The faint outer detail is lost because of the bright background sky. There is no doubt, however, that this galaxy has the same soft "massive" arms as 4826, 4569, and 4579. The internal dust lanes are quite regular. The most conspicuous lane does not start in the nuclear region but begins abruptly some distance from the center—an unusual feature in galaxies.

NGC 5005   Sb
H–2170–H
June 29/30, 1941
Cr-Hi-Sp-Sp
45 min
Enlarged 3.6×

This galaxy is not of the 4569 type but is illustrated here to show the prominent dust lane similar to the one in 4450 (above). As in 4450, the lane does not begin in the nuclear region but rather on the periphery of the high-surface-brightness central region. This central region is not amorphous but contains a spiral structure traceable to within 7 sec of arc (2 mm on the illustration) of the center. Dust lanes and luminous spiral filaments are present to within this distance. The rather abrupt change of surface brightness from the outer to the inner spiral arms (which occurs at a radius of 8 mm from the center on this illustration) is similar to the same feature in NGC 5055 (p. *15*), 3521 (p. *15*), 4699 (p. *16*), 1068 (p. *16*), and others.

13

14

NGC 2841   Sb
PH–60–MH
Feb. 14/15, 1950
103aO
30 min
Enlarged 7.5×

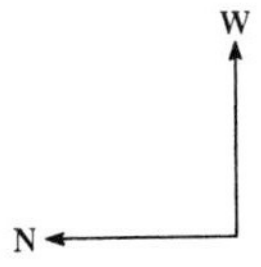

W ↑

N ←

This is the type example of the multiple-arm Sb sub-group. NGC 2841 is the earliest of the group. All galaxies illustrated on pages *14* to *19* are of this type.

NGC 2841 has a central region composed of a bright nucleus (smaller than 15 sec of arc in diameter) and an amorphous lens devoid of dust or spiral structure. The lens resembles an E or $S0_1$ galaxy. The smooth lens has a major diameter of 100 sec (60 mm on this illustration). Multiple, thin dust lanes begin to spiral outward at the periphery of the amorphous lens. They appear to separate luminous spiral filaments of very complex structure. At first glance the filaments look like complete spiral arms, but closer inspection shows that only thin broken segments are present which cannot be traced as individual arcs for more than 30°.

NGC 4826   M64   Sb
Ri–65 (60″)
May 5, 6, 7, 8, 1910
7 hr 56 min
Enlarged 3.7✕

NGC 4826 is the earliest Sb shown in the atlas. This plate was taken by Ritchey in a four-night exposure with the 60-inch. Note the very soft texture to the spiral arms. These arms are nearly circular, and they show no trace of resolution into knots. NGC 4826 is classed as Sb rather than as Sa because of the very heavy dust lane in the center, which is shown below.

NGC 4826   M64   Sb
Ri–58 (60″)
Mar. 8/9, 1910
240 min
Enlarged 3.7✕

This is a shorter exposure of NGC 4826 than the one shown above. The dust pattern in the nucleus is very prominent. The bright filaments, which make up the inner spiral structure, are also visible. Although the strongest concentration of the dust is in a single dark lane, a fainter dust arm can be seen on the inner edge of the last luminous arm on the north side of the galaxy in this illustration.

NGC 4569   M90   Sb
PH–12–Bm
Jan. 31/Feb. 1, 1952
103aO + WG2
30 min
Enlarged 2.0✕

The soft texture of the spiral arms and the heavy dust lanes near the center of this galaxy are similar to these features in 4826 (left). Spiral arms of this type were described as "massive" by Reynolds and by Hubble. Dust lanes can be traced almost to the nucleus, which is of high surface brightness and about 2 mm in diameter on the scale of this illustration. There is partial resolution of one of the inner dust lanes into knots, which are presumed to be H II regions.

NGC 4579   M58   Sb/SBb
PH–28–Bm
Mar. 31/Apr. 1, 1952
103aO + WG2
30 min
Enlarged 2.8✕

This galaxy is a much later example of the 4569 subgroup than 4826 or 4569 itself. There are two very faint outer spiral arms which are smooth in texture and are "massive" in the sense of the spiral arms in 4826 and 4569. They do not show well in the illustration because of their low surface brightness. Two thin dust lanes can be traced in this outer region near the smooth, massive arm, on the north side of the galaxy. More prominent dust lanes, thin and well defined, can be traced on the inside of the bright inner spiral arms. There is a bar of enhanced luminosity across the central amorphous region, though it is not well enough defined to classify NGC 4579 as an SBb. The galaxy is a transition between Sb and SBb. Note the partial resolution of the arms into knots.

NGC 4450   Sb
H–2432–H
May 17/18, 1947
103aO
25 min
Enlarged 4.0✕

This galaxy is an intermediate case of the 4826 group. The plate was taken with the 100-inch after the war, when the city lights from Los Angeles were bright. The faint outer detail is lost because of the bright background sky. There is no doubt, however, that this galaxy has the same soft "massive" arms as 4826, 4569, and 4579. The internal dust lanes are quite regular. The most conspicuous lane does not start in the nuclear region but begins abruptly some distance from the center—an unusual feature in galaxies.

NGC 5005   Sb
H–2170–H
June 29/30, 1941
Cr-Hi-Sp-Sp
45 min
Enlarged 3.6✕

This galaxy is not of the 4569 type but is illustrated here to show the prominent dust lane similar to the one in 4450 (above). As in 4450, the lane does not begin in the nuclear region but rather on the periphery of the high-surface-brightness central region. This central region is not amorphous but contains a spiral structure traceable to within 7 sec of arc (2 mm on the illustration) of the center. Dust lanes and luminous spiral filaments are present to within this distance. The rather abrupt change of surface brightness from the outer to the inner spiral arms (which occurs at a radius of 8 mm from the center on this illustration) is similar to the same feature in NGC 5055 (p. *15*), 3521 (p. *15*), 4699 (p. *16*), 1068 (p. *16*), and others.

13

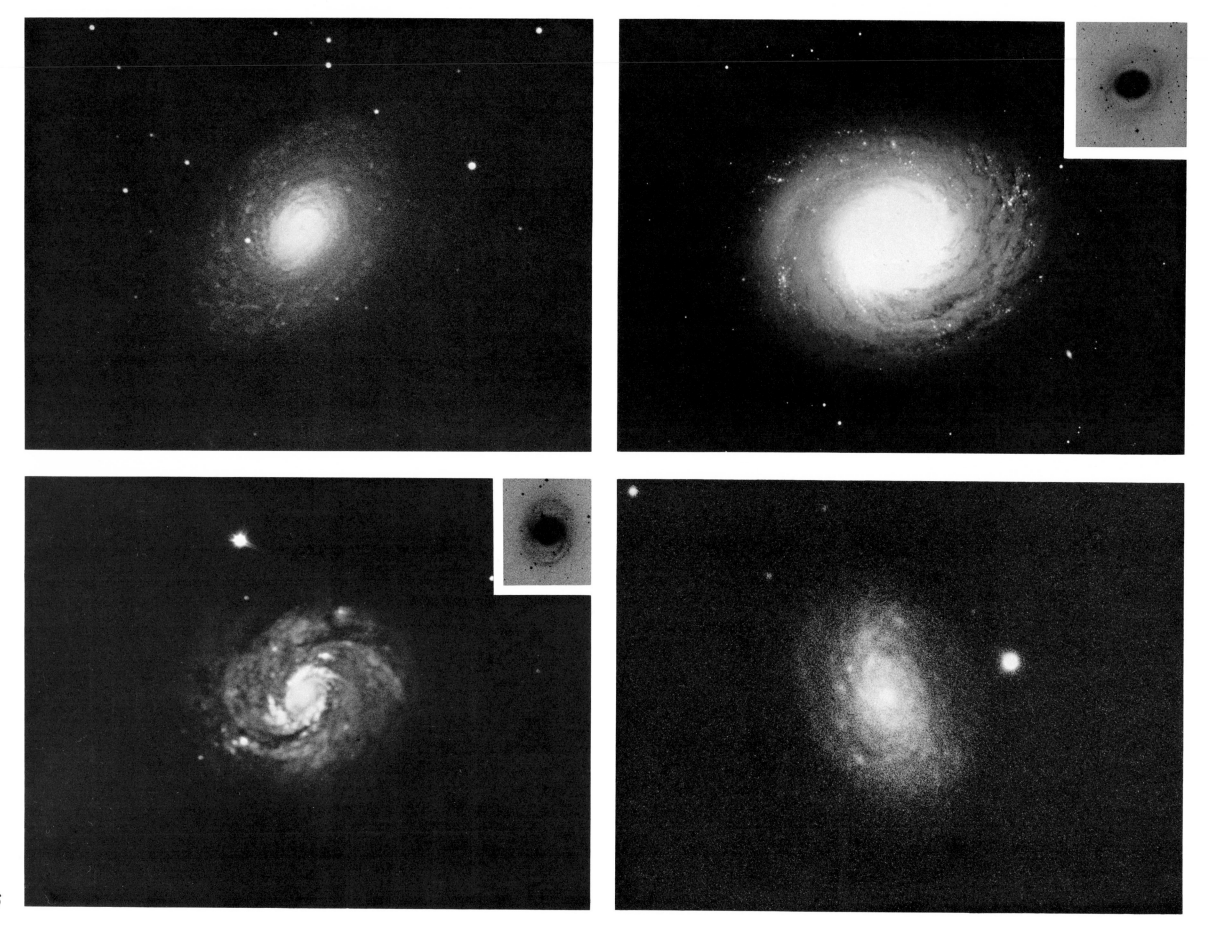

NGC 4699   Sb
H–2523–H
Mar. 7/8, 1948
103aO
30 min
Enlarged 6.0×

Very closely packed and tightly wound spiral arms can be traced to within 12 sec of arc from the center, corresponding to about 4 mm on the scale of this illustration. Note the difference in surface brightness between the inner and the outer regions. The important point, emphasized in the description of 5055, is that spiral arms exist in this inner region of high surface brightness.

NGC 1068   M77   Sb
H–2336–H
Nov. 27/28, 1946
IIaO
10 min
Enlarged 8.0×

This is the type example for galaxies with a discontinuity of surface brightness between the inner and outer regions. The spiral arms are not as thin as in 2841, 488, 7217, 5055, 3521, or 4699. Two principal dust arms can be traced on this illustration. The luminous spiral arms can be seen to within 6 sec (radius) from the center. The inner arms are resolved into knots. This galaxy has broad emission lines in the spectrum of the nuclear region (Seyfert, *Ap. J.*, *97*, 28, 1943). Faint external spiral arms of low surface brightness and amorphous texture are shown in the insert.

NGC 4736   M94   Sb
PH–423–MH
Apr. 15/16, 1952
103aO
30 min
Enlarged 3.2×

The range of surface brightness between the nuclear region and the outer regions, including the external ring, is very great. This illustration does not show the complex structure of the galaxy. The intense central region is devoid of spiral structure. It is 32 sec of arc in diameter (8 mm on the illustration). Tightly wound spiral arms of the kind seen in NGC 4699 (left) begin tangent to this amorphous central region and wind out through a region of lower surface brightness of lens shape with a diameter of 120 sec of arc (35 mm on the illustration). Details of structure in both these regions are invisible here because of the inability of photographic paper to reproduce large intensity differences. A third region, filled with spiral arms, begins at the outer boundary of the second zone. As between the first and second zones, a sharp discontinuity of surface brightness exists between the second and third zones. The spiral structure in the third zone is seen in the illustration. The surface brightness of the third zone appears to go to zero rather suddenly 200 sec of arc from the center. An annular zone devoid of luminosity then begins. This zone of near zero surface brightness continues until the inner boundary of a faint external ring is reached at 260 sec of arc radius from the nucleus. The ring is shown in the insert. It has a fairly sharp inner boundary but fades and is lost in the night-sky radiation at large distances from the center. The ring is not detached from the nuclear region but is connected to the more central regions on the west side.

NGC 4800   Sb
S–1807–H
May 24/25, 1938
Agfa Blue
60 min
Enlarged 19.2×

NGC 4800 is of the same type as 5055, 4699, etc. This illustration is from a 60-inch plate greatly enlarged. Spiral arms can be traced to within 3 sec of arc of the center (2 mm on the illustration). There is a discontinuity in the surface brightness of the inner and the outer regions similar to that in other members of this group.

NGC 3031   M81   Sb   → N
PH–421–MH
Apr. 15/16, 1952   ↓
103aO   W
30 min
Enlarged 3.0×

M81 has a large amorphous central region in which there
is no suggestion of resolution into individual stars. There
is no doubt that this region resembles the central part of
M31 and that, under the proper conditions, with a large
telescope, M81 could be resolved into stars just as Baade
resolved M31. The distance modulus of M81 is about
$m - M = 27.1$ (Sandage, *A. J.*, *59*, 180, 1954). If $M_V =$
-3.0 for the brightest stars in the central lens, then $m_V =$
24.1. This is beyond the limits of the 200-inch telescope
with the Ross $f/3.67$ lens. Two possibilities exist, however, for achieving the resolution of M81. We can use the
$f/4.85$ lens, which will give about a 1-magnitude increase
in the limit, and we can go to the infrared where the absolute magnitude for these globular-cluster-like stars is undoubtedly brighter than -3.0.

Dust lanes, forming a multiple spiral pattern, thread
through the central region and are silhouetted against the
amorphous, luminous background. These fainter multiple dust lanes do not show in the illustration because of
the overexposed central region. They can be traced to
within 35 sec of arc from the center (8 mm on this illustration) along the major axis.

The outer dust lanes lie on the inside of the luminous
spiral arms. These arms are thin, moderately well defined,
and branched near the ends of the major axis. Note the
intricate dust pattern at the south-following (southeast)
end of the major axis. There is an even more intricate
pattern of straight dust lanes, which has no connection
with the spiral structure, on the north-preceding end of
the major axis. The parallel streaks can be traced across
the central lens and across two branches of the brighter
spiral arm on the north-preceding side.

The arms are highly resolved into individual stars and
H II regions. The stellar contents of M81 are similar to
the contents of M31. Twenty-five normal novae have been
found; three variables which are definitely cepheids, fifteen other variables which are probably cepheids, seven
irregular blue variables of the type known in M31 and
M33, and a number of irregular red variables are known.
All these stars are brighter than $M_{pg} = -4.5$.

19

NGC 224   M31   Sb
PS-0-H
48ʺ Schmidt
Sept. 29/30, 1948
103aO
10 min
Enlarged 2.5×

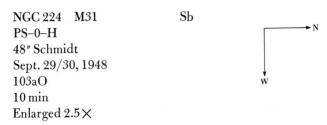

M31 is probably of the 2841 type of multiple-arm galaxy although it differs from such type examples as 488, 5055, and 4699. The arms in M31 are thicker and less well defined than in these prototypes. Baade has made a long and careful study of M31, both of its geometric form and of its stellar content. A short description of part of this work is given by Baade in his report to the Rome Conference on Stellar Populations (vol. 5 of *Ricerche astronomiche, spècola vaticana*, 1958, pp. 3–21). Baade has noted seven distinct spiral arms in M31 (see table 2 of his report). The inner two arms are dust arms; the outer five arms contain supergiant O and B stars. The first two arms cross the north-following half of the major axis at distances of 3.4 and 8.0 sec of arc from the center. These angles correspond to 1.5 mm and 3.6 mm from the center on the scale of the illustration. Both arms, designated as N1 and N2 by Baade, are within the burned-out central region of the illustration.

The texture of the background luminosity of the central portion of M31 is smooth and amorphous on plates taken with small telescopes. Baade has shown, however, that this central region can be resolved into red stars whose color indices are about international 1.3 and whose absolute magnitudes are about $M_V = -3.0$ (Baade, *Ap. J.*, *100*, 79, 1944). The resolved images resemble those in NGC 205, which is the E5 companion galaxy west of the center of M31. NGC 205 is illustrated on page *3* of this atlas.

Dust lanes and dust patches are present in the central region of M31. Again, these are not visible on the illustration. But a negative print of lower density is reproduced by Hubble and Sandage in *Ap. J.*, *118*, 353, 1953 (fig. 2). The dust arms and patches are similar to those in NGC 3031 (M81) shown on page *19* of this atlas.

The distance modulus of M31 is probably close to $m - M = 24.6$ (Th. Schmidt, *Z. Astrophys.*, *41*, 182, 1957; Sandage, *Ap. J.*, *127*, 513, 1958). The limiting photographic magnitude of the 48-inch Schmidt telescope is $m_{pg} = 21.1$ (Abell, *Ap. J.*, *Supp. Sec.*, *III*, 211, 1958). Therefore all resolved stars on this illustration are brighter than $M_{pg} = -3.5$.

NGC 3031   M81   Sb

PH–421–MH
Apr. 15/16, 1952
103aO
30 min
Enlarged 3.0✕

M81 has a large amorphous central region in which there is no suggestion of resolution into individual stars. There is no doubt that this region resembles the central part of M31 and that, under the proper conditions, with a large telescope, M81 could be resolved into stars just as Baade resolved M31. The distance modulus of M81 is about $m - M = 27.1$ (Sandage, *A. J.*, *59*, 180, 1954). If $M_V = -3.0$ for the brightest stars in the central lens, then $m_V = 24.1$. This is beyond the limits of the 200-inch telescope with the Ross $f/3.67$ lens. Two possibilities exist, however, for achieving the resolution of M81. We can use the $f/4.85$ lens, which will give about a 1-magnitude increase in the limit, and we can go to the infrared where the absolute magnitude for these globular-cluster-like stars is undoubtedly brighter than –3.0.

Dust lanes, forming a multiple spiral pattern, thread through the central region and are silhouetted against the amorphous, luminous background. These fainter multiple dust lanes do not show in the illustration because of the overexposed central region. They can be traced to within 35 sec of arc from the center (8 mm on this illustration) along the major axis.

The outer dust lanes lie on the inside of the luminous spiral arms. These arms are thin, moderately well defined, and branched near the ends of the major axis. Note the intricate dust pattern at the south-following (southeast) end of the major axis. There is an even more intricate pattern of straight dust lanes, which has no connection with the spiral structure, on the north-preceding end of the major axis. The parallel streaks can be traced across the central lens and across two branches of the brighter spiral arm on the north-preceding side.

The arms are highly resolved into individual stars and H II regions. The stellar contents of M81 are similar to the contents of M31. Twenty-five normal novae have been found; three variables which are definitely cepheids, fifteen other variables which are probably cepheids, seven irregular blue variables of the type known in M31 and M33, and a number of irregular red variables are known. All these stars are brighter than $M_{pg} = -4.5$.

NGC 6384   Sb/SBb
H–2259–H
May 3/4, 1946
103aO
40 min
Enlarged 3.2✕

This and the two galaxies shown in the panels immediately to the right form an intermediate group between the multiple-arm systems like 2841 and 488 of the Sb and the M101 group of the Sc section. The arms in 6384 are thin and tightly wound about an amorphous nuclear region. There is a distinct bar of enhanced surface brightness crossing the central lens along the major axis of the spiral pattern. NGC 6384 is a transition case to SBb.

NGC 4237   Sb
H–1970–H
Apr. 21/22, 1938
E40
60 min
Enlarged 8.3✕

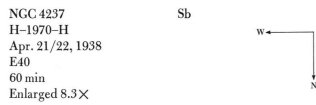

The three galaxies shown on this bottom panel form a subgroup of Sb similar to the NGC 253–2903 group of Sc (pp. *34* and *35* of the atlas). The arms are not well separated from each other, and they are difficult to trace. They start at the small compact nucleus. Considerable dust is spread throughout the fundamental plane, and the dust arms define the spiral pattern fully as well as the luminous arms between the dust lanes.

NGC 6814   Sb
PH–236–B
Sept. 11/12, 1950
103aO + GG1
30 min
Enlarged 5.0✕

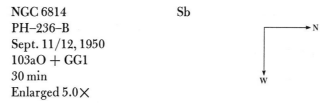

Notice the tightly wound multiple arms of this galaxy. They are thicker than those of 2841, and the nuclear region is smaller. The arms are highly branched. Each of the arms is of almost uniform surface brightness for about one complete revolution, at which point there is a sharp break in the brightness. Fainter extensions of the arm system can be traced on the outside of the brighter arms. The same phenomenon occurs in many galaxies such as 6384 (left) and 3147 (right).

NGC 7392   Sb
H–1854–H
Aug. 3/4, 1937
Imp. Ecl.
60 min
Enlarged 8.0✕

Although there are two principal arms to this galaxy, much internal spiral structure exists up to the amorphous central region, which is 5 mm in diameter on the scale of the illustration.

NGC 3147   Sb
S–1910–H
Jan. 27/28, 1946
103aO
60 min
Enlarged 8.2✕

This galaxy is similar to 6814. Tightly wound multiple arms are present, which can be traced to within 8 sec of arc (2.5 mm on the illustration) from the small, amorphous nucleus. The details of the structure are not too clear on this reproduction from a poor 60-inch plate. The arms are highly branched. Note the faint-surface-brightness arm on the outside of the bright arm on the north side. Whenever two arm systems of different surface brightness occur, the fainter set is always on the outside.

NGC 4062   Sb
H–2246–H
Mar. 7/8, 1946
103aO
60 min
Enlarged 4.1✕

The dust lanes are very conspicuous in 4062 because of its high inclination to the line of sight. These are multiple spiral arms. The structure closely resembles that of 5055 in its outer regions (p. *15*). The nucleus of 4062 is very small, only 2 mm in diameter on the scale of the illustration. As in 6384 and 6814, the outer spiral arms are fainter than those close to the nucleus.

NGC 4750   Sb
S–458–H
Mar. 18/19, 1925
E40
55 min
Enlarged 22.2×

All galaxies on the facing page form a special subgroup, in which the spiral pattern emerges tangent to what appears to be an external ring rather than from the nucleus. The ring in 4750 appears to be completely detached from the central nucleus and lens. It is probably composed of two overlapping spiral fragments wound so tightly as nearly to overlap. A very faint external pattern is present, which is shown, but to poor advantage, by the insert, taken with the 48-inch Schmidt.

NGC 4580   Sb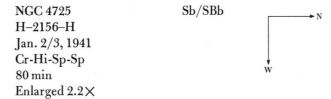
H–2285–H
May 30/31, 1946
103aO
40 min
Enlarged 12.1×

The internal "ring" in this galaxy must be very similar to that in 3705, but it is more easily seen here because 4580 is more nearly face on. The ring is really two closely coiled spiral arms of high surface brightness. The connections that these arms make with the nucleus are not well defined and cannot be traced. The arms appear to begin tangent to the edge of the central lens. Three faint external arms of smooth texture can be seen in the insert. Two of the three arms are continuations of the inner ring arms; the other comes off at a peculiar angle.

NGC 1832   Sb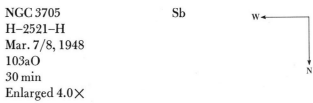
PH–70–H
Oct. 13/14, 1950
103aO
30 min
Enlarged 5.0×

The internal ring is quite conspicuous in 1832. It is not completely closed but is of the type best illustrated in NGC 1073 (p. *49*). Note the branching of the spiral arms on the west side. The two prominent dust lanes are on the inside of the main spiral arms. The arms are resolved into knots, which are probably H II regions rather than individual stars. The central region of 1832 shows some characteristics of a bar.

NGC 4725   Sb/SBb
H–2156–H
Jan. 2/3, 1941
Cr-Hi-Sp-Sp
80 min
Enlarged 2.2×

This is a transition galaxy between a normal Sb and an SBb. The region of enhanced luminosity across the central lens is not a well defined bar as in 1398 (p. *47*). The basic nebular type is closer to Sb than SBb. The internal "ring" is not complete but resembles that in NGC 4580. It begins abruptly at the edge of the amorphous central region and breaks into multiple, tightly wound spiral arms in the southeast quadrant. The dust lanes are seen silhouetted against the background light especially well in this quadrant. The inner arms are resolved into knots. Two faint external arms are present, which can be traced in the insert. These arms are smooth in texture with no hint of resolution into knots. The external arms are not on opposite sides of the nucleus but travel together, one lapped on the inside of the other. Careful inspection of the insert picture will separate the two, although on small-scale plates they will appear as a single arm.

A supernova was discovered in 4725 on May 5, 1940, by J. J. Johnson at Palomar (Harv. Ann. Card 522). Two photographs of NGC 4725 which show the supernova appear on the back cover of *The Sky*, February 1941. The supernova can still be seen on this plate taken by Hubble in January 1941, some 9 months after outburst.

NGC 3705   Sb
H–2521–H
Mar. 7/8, 1948
103aO
30 min
Enlarged 4.0×

The internal ring resembles the similar feature in 4274 (Sa, p. *12*). As in 4274, the ring is probably two overlapping spiral arms which just miss each other after a half revolution. The outer arms are of lower surface brightness than the ring. They either start at the ring or are a continuation of the ends of the arms composing the ring. In this respect also 3705 is similar to 4274.

NGC 3145   Sb
H–2350–H
Nov. 28/29, 1946
103aO
30 min
Enlarged 8.1×

The thin multiple arms of this galaxy are complex. The brightest arms in the northwest quadrant appear to approach the nucleus at right angles (tangent rather than spiraling inward). There is a single faint arm in the southwest quadrant which crosses one of the regular arms nearly at right angles. This is a very rare feature of galaxies and is particularly well shown here. A few dust lanes can be seen near the crossover point.

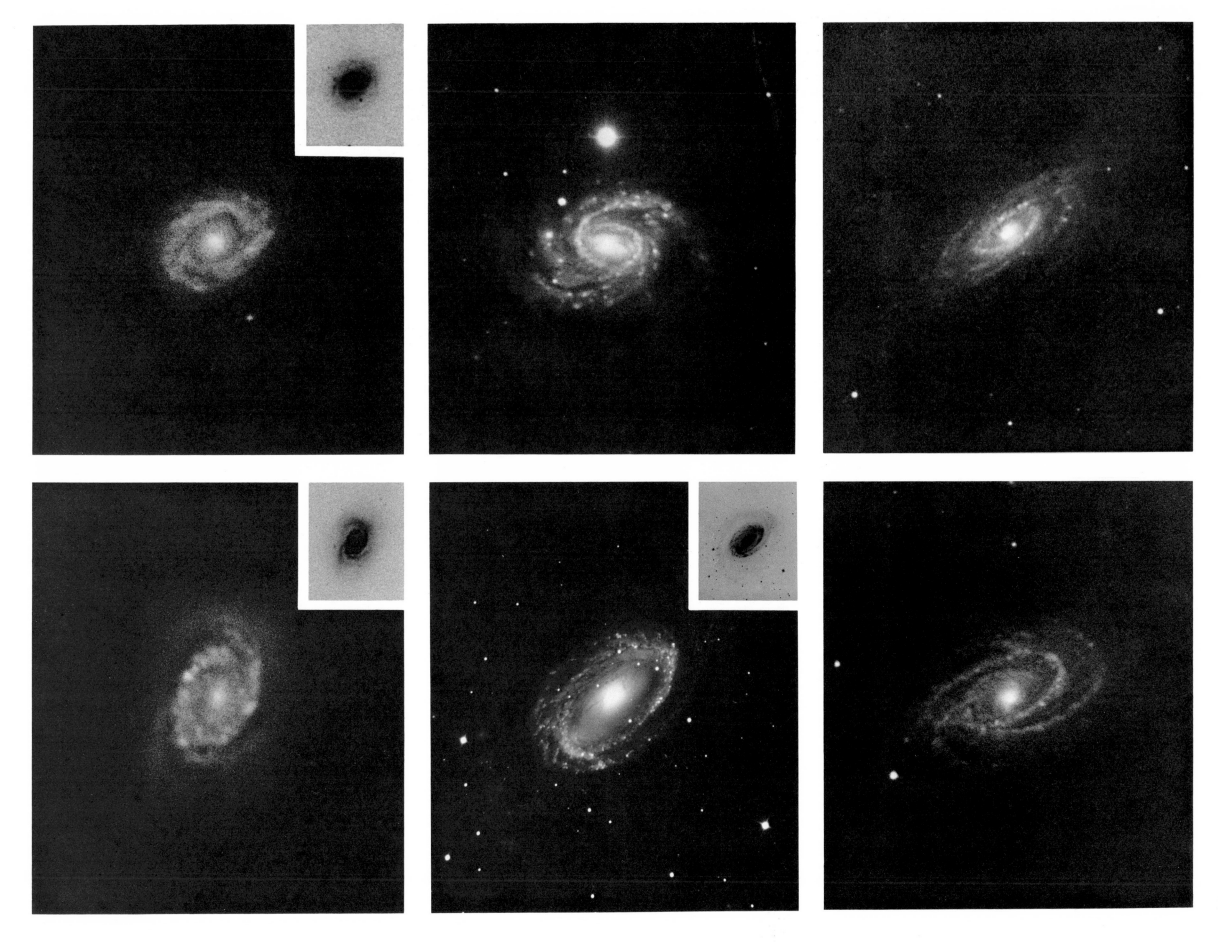

22

NGC 23   Sb
PH–1039–S
Aug. 22/23, 1955
103aO
30 min
Enlarged 16.0✕

This galaxy is probably of the NGC 210 subgroup of Sb. Two sets of arms are present, the inner set being tightly wound and the outer more loosely wound. At first glance there seems to be only one outer arm, but in the insert photograph a faint and more diffuse arm can just be seen starting near the bright star at the southeast end of the major axis. One conspicuous dust lane is present in the central region, on the inside of one of the inner arms. Although NGC 23 is not a good example of the NGC 210 group of Sb, the characteristic feature of two sets of spiral arms of different pitch is present. A supernova appeared in this galaxy in 1955. It was discovered on a plate taken with the 200-inch on October 22/23, 1955.

NGC 210   Sb
PH–1075–S
Aug. 25/26, 1955
103aO
30 min
Enlarged 4.0✕

This is the type example for the four galaxies shown on the page. Each of the four galaxies has two sets of spiral arms. The inner set is tightly wound around the nucleus and is not resolved into stars or knots. The outer set is open and well defined, and is usually partially resolved. The inner lens is of high surface brightness but contains spiral structure. In this sense the group resembles NGC 5055. Note the two prominent dust lanes in the nuclear region. The outer spiral arms in this galaxy are branched as in M101.

NGC 1964   Sb
PH–1142–S
Oct. 23/24, 1955
103aO + WG2
25 min
Enlarged 4.0✕

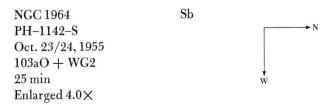

This galaxy is seen at a high angle of projection. In form it is almost identical to NGC 210. Prominent dust lanes and spiral structure are present in the bright central lens. These inner spiral arms are tightly wound. The two outer spiral arms start tangent to the inner lens and wind through about 300° before they can be traced no longer. They show partial resolution. The plate from which this reproduction was made was taken under poor seeing conditions.

NGC 615   Sb
PH–1077–S
Aug. 25/26, 1955
103aO
30 min
Enlarged 7.0✕

This galaxy is similar to NGC 1964 and NGC 210. The inner spiral structure and the prominent dust lanes can be seen in the bright central lens on the original plate. There are only two outer arms in this galaxy, but they are considerably thicker than the arms of 210. Each of the outer arms can be traced through about 360°. One arm, coming from the periphery of the lens, approaches close to the inner edge of the other arm after the first arm has turned about 180°. This apparent overlapping of the arms is similar to the pattern in NGC 3185 (p. *43*), 4274 (p. *12*), and others.

NGC 3627   M66   Sb
H–527–H
Jan. 30/31, 1925
E40
90 min
Enlarged 7.2×

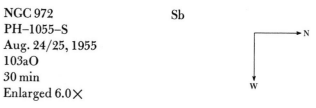

NGC 3627 and the other two galaxies shown on the page contain a great deal of dust. Since dust cannot be detected in galaxies unless it is silhouetted against a bright background, it shows best in galaxies that are highly inclined to the line of sight. Numerous good examples are shown in the atlas, among which we mention 2841 (p. *14*), 5055 (p. *15*), 3521 (p. *15*), 7331 (p. *17*), M31 (p. *18*), 4594 (p. *24*), all the galaxies on page *25*, M83 (p. *28*), and the nuclei of M51 and M101 (p. *31*). The dust pattern in NGC 3627 is particularly heavy. The lane going from the southeast to the northeast quadrant is located on the inner edge of the luminous spiral arm. The lane associated with the opposite arm bisects the luminous matter.

The contrast of the reproduction is high. On the original plate, faint dust lanes are scattered throughout the central lens and between the outer arms and the nuclear regions.

NGC 972   Sb
PH–1055–S
Aug. 24/25, 1955
103aO
30 min
Enlarged 6.0×

The dust lanes are scattered in an almost chaotic fashion across the face of NGC 972. The image looks almost like an irregular galaxy of the M82 type (p. *41*). However, a general spiral pattern can be traced with two sets of dust lanes: the prominent dust arm is in the southeast quadrant; the second arm can be seen partly silhouetted in the northwest quadrant. This galaxy is important to settle the question of the direction of the spiral pattern with respect to the rotation vector. The direction of rotation, however, is unknown.

NGC 4433   Sb
PH–1171–S
Dec. 14/15, 1955
103aO
30 min
Enlarged 9.0×

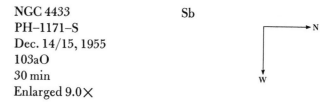

The dust is scattered chaotically across the face of 4433. It is difficult to trace spiral arms in the inner region shown in the illustration. Note the straight, luminous filament on the west side. Two very faint spiral arms, smooth in texture and of low surface brightness, can be traced outside the main body. They do not show in the illustration.

23

NGC 4594   M104   Sa/Sb
PH–96–MH
Mar. 16/17, 1950
103aO
30 min
Enlarged 6.6×

N

W

NGC 4594 is very difficult to classify because the fundamental plane is inclined only 6° to the line of sight. The most prominent feature of the photographic image is the dust lane that defines the fundamental plane. It is significant for the physics of the problem that most or all of the dust in any galaxy is confined to a very thin plane, which undoubtedly is the plane perpendicular to the angular momentum vector. This statement concerning the dust can be made from the observational data in only those galaxies whose fundamental planes are nearly in the line of sight. Other examples of such galaxies are shown on page *25*.

A remarkable picture of NGC 4594 was published by Lindblad from a plate taken by Baade in ultraviolet light (*Pubs. A. S. P.*, *63*, 133, 1951). The knots and segments of spiral arms can be seen in this photograph. These knots, together with what appear to be almost circular spiral arms, suggest a face-on spiral pattern like that in NGC 488 or possibly 5055.

Another notable feature of NGC 4594 is the large central nuclear bulge. The tight spiral pattern, which of course is nearly impossible to trace, and the large nuclear bulge place NGC 4594 as either a late Sa or a very early Sb.

There appears to be a concentration of stars or nebular images in the halo of 4594. These are believed to be globular clusters similar to those found throughout the image of 4486 (M87, p. *2*). The number of clusters in 4594 is far below that in M87. The distance modulus of about $m - M = 30.6$ for 4594 together with a threshold of about $m = 20$ for these images puts the absolute magnitude of the brightest condensation at $M_{pg} = -10.6$, which matches the brightest globular clusters in our own galaxy.

NGC 4565   Sb
PH–163–MH
Apr. 15/16, 1950
103aE
25 min
Enlarged 1.2×

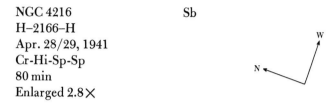

All galaxies on the facing page are nearly on edge. The pictures show the change in the nuclear bulge along the sequence of classification and the concentration of the dust to a fundamental plane. Note how flat the central cross section of 4565 is. The nuclear bulge is not so large as that of NGC 4594 but is larger than that of 891. 4594 is an Sa or very early Sb. 4565 is classed as an intermediate Sb, and 891 as a very late Sb. De Vaucouleurs illustrates and discusses 4565, 4216, and others in his article on the direction of tilt (*Ap. J.*, *127*, 487, 1958).

NGC 4244   Sc
PH–151–MH
Apr. 12/13, 1950
103aO
30 min
Enlarged 0.89×

NGC 4244 is undoubtedly a late Sc galaxy seen on edge. There is no nuclear bulge; the entire surface is resolved into stars; and the dust lanes, although present, are not at all conspicuous. This galaxy must be near by because it is resolved into stars throughout its surface. They are individual stars and not H II regions. The reproduction is too overexposed to show the resolution in the nuclear region which is visible on the original plate. The estimated distance modulus of 4244 is between $m - M = 26.5$ and $m - M = 27.0$. The galaxy is more distant than members of the Local Group but not so distant as the M81 and M101 groups.

NGC 4216   Sb
H–2166–H
Apr. 28/29, 1941
Cr-Hi-Sp-Sp
80 min
Enlarged 2.8×

This magnificent spiral is inclined to the line of sight at just the correct angle to show both the nuclear bulge and the spiral dust pattern in the fundamental plane. The impressive datum is the thinness of the plane. This galaxy is important for the problem of direction of tilt. A negative print is shown by Hubble (*Ap. J.*, *97*, 225, 1943) and by de Vaucouleurs. NGC 4216 is probably an intermediate Sb.

NGC 5907   Sc
PH–186–MH
May 10/11, 1950
103aO
40 min
Enlarged 1.3×

NGC 5907 is an early Sc galaxy seen within a few degrees of edge on. The nuclear bulge is quite small and is almost hidden behind the opaque dust lane. It appears that the outermost spiral arms can be seen at either end of the spindle, and their sense of opening can be inferred. The arm on the north side is opening toward the observer (out of the page); the arm on the south side is going away (into the page). Spectroscopic observations show that the south end of the spindle is approaching. This means that the arms are trailing.

NGC 891   Sb
PH–208–S
Nov. 10/11, 1952
103aO + WG2
30 min
Enlarged 1.2×

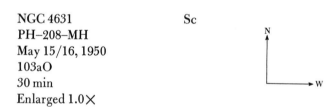

The nuclear bulge in 891 is smaller than that in 4565. The galaxy is classed as late Sb. The dust lane has a very intricate pattern perpendicular to the plane. Thin fingers of obscuration extend at least 30 sec of arc in the Z direction. The distance modulus of 891 is about $m - M = 29.0$, assuming membership in the NGC 1023 kinematical group (Humason et al., *A. J.*, *61*, 97, 1956, table XI) and a Hubble constant of 75 km/sec 10^6 parsecs. At this distance, 30 sec of arc corresponds to 105 parsecs. Energy must be pumped into the dust to keep it distended this far above the plane against the potential energy of the gravitational field. It is believed that NGC 891 is similar to our own galaxy. See the photograph of the dust band in the plane of our galaxy compared with NGC 891 by Osterbrock and Sharpless (*Ap. J.*, *115*, 140, 1952). See also the infrared photographs of Code and Houck, *Ap. J.*, *121*, 533, 1955.

NGC 4631   Sc
PH–208–MH
May 15/16, 1950
103aO
30 min
Enlarged 1.0×

NGC 4631 is probably a late Sc. There is no sign of a nuclear bulge. The entire surface is resolved into stars and H II regions. There are many dust patches but no strong dust lane across the spindle as in 4565 or 891. The small companion galaxy north of 4631 is NGC 4627, an E5 or S0₁ galaxy with indication of globular clusters surrounding the main body. It is likely that 4627 forms a dynamical unit with 4631 similar to the M32, NGC 205, M31 system. However, no redshift is available for NGC 4627.

26

NGC 5194/5195   M51   Sc/Irr
PH–201–MH
May 14/15, 1950   W
103aO
20 min   N ←
Enlarged 4.8×

NGC 5194 is one of the most magnificent spirals in the sky. The entire spiral pattern is dominated by the dust lanes. The two most opaque dust lanes lie on the inside of the two brightest spiral arms. These two principal arms plus their associated dust lanes wind into the central region along an almost perfect spiral path. The dust arms are very highly branched. Thin filaments break away from the main dust path and cross the luminous arms almost at right angles. Multiple secondary dust lanes exist throughout the central lens. Individual dust lanes of the secondary pattern cannot be traced, but, rather, separate segments exist which, when viewed with other segments, form a rough spiral structure. The two main arms can be traced for one and a half revolutions. Branching occurs from one luminous arm to the other after about three-quarters of a revolution. Each branch continues as a separate arm, giving the spiral the appearance of having a multiple-arm structure. Actually the multiplicity is not like that of 2841 or 488 because, in these, two main arms cannot be traced but the multiple filaments begin immediately at the periphery of the amorphous central lens.

The companion galaxy NGC 5195 is an Irr of the M82 type. The dust from the northeast arm of 5194 crosses in front of 5195 on the eastern edge, but there are dust patches internal to 5195 itself on the west side. NGC 5195 closely resembles NGC 3077 (p. 41) and M82. Holmberg has found the international color index of the companion to be 0.98. This is redder than his measures of M82 (CI = 0.81) and 3077 (CI = 0.68), but part of the redness may be due to internal absorption. NGC 5194 is close enough to us to be easily resolved into stars along the spiral arms. Many H II regions are present. No clusters, either globular or open, have been identified with certainty. The distance modulus of these two galaxies must be about $m - M = 27.5$, which is slightly more distant than the M81 group.

Negative photographs of NGC 5194/5195 showing the dust lanes in both galaxies to good advantage have been published by Zwicky (*Pubs. A. S. P.*, *67*, 232, 1955). Also the characteristics of the two principal luminous arms are well revealed by a superposition trick of negatives taken in different colors. Plate IV of Zwicky's paper shows the intricate dust lanes quite well.

The details of the dust lanes in the center of 5194 are of interest. The nuclear regions are shown on page *31* of this atlas.

NGC 5457   M101   Sc
PH–152–B
July 17/18, 1950
103aO
30 min
Enlarged 2.6×

M101 is the prototype of the multiple-arm galaxies of the Sc section. Although many separate arms exist in the outer regions, each one can be traced from a branching of two principal dust arms which begin in the nucleus. This dust pattern is shown in the illustration of the central region on page *31*. As in M51, many dust arms exist in the central lens. They cannot be traced as individual arms but rather as separate segments which, when taken together, form a rough spiral pattern. The entire spiral pattern over the face of M51 is dominated by the dust lanes, which usually are on the inside of the bright luminous spiral filaments. The outer segments of the luminous arms are thoroughly resolved into individual stars and a few H II regions. The outer arms are highly branched. The surface brightness of the arms in the northwest quadrant of the spiral is very low, and the resolved stars in these arms are faint. The brightest arms are in the southwest quadrant. Notice the resolved clumps or associations of stars in the brightest arm on the east side. The most conspicuous of the associations is elliptical, with a major and minor axis of 50 sec and 15 sec of arc, respectively. The distance modulus of M101 is about 27.0, which makes the linear dimensions of the association about 620 parsecs by 190 parsecs. The average width of an arm is about 30 sec of arc, corresponding to 380 parsecs. The largest H II regions are about 10 sec of arc in diameter, which corresponds to 120 parsecs. This is smaller by about a factor of 6 than the 30 Doradus complex in the Large Magellanic Cloud and smaller by about a factor of 3 than NGC 604 in M33. 30 Doradus is about 640 parsecs in diameter; NGC 604, about 320 parsecs.

Many Sc galaxies are of the M101 type. The characteristics of the type are (1) a small nucleus from which the spiral pattern emerges in dust lanes, at first, and farther out in luminous filaments; (2) multiple spiral arms, thin and highly branched in their outer regions; (3) arms well resolved into individual stars and H II regions.

The integrated color indices of Sc galaxies are instructive. Erik Holmberg has measured magnitudes and colors for a number of galaxies, and his results have direct bearing on the classification problem. Spirals like M101, in which the entire structure is dominated by the spiral arms, have blue colors. M101 itself has an international color index of 0.30. Most of the galaxies on page *29* have colors in the range 0.30 to 0.50. The more open, chaotic spirals like M101 or NGC 628 (p. *29*) are bluer than spirals like 4321 (M100, p. *28*).

NGC 4321   M100   Sc
PH–743–S
Apr. 8/9, 1954
103aD + GG14
60 min
Enlarged 5.2×

NGC 5236   M83   Sc/SBb
H–540–H
Mar. 2/3, 1925
E40
100 min
Enlarged 3.3×

NGC 4321 is the brightest spiral in the Virgo Cluster. The galaxy has characteristics of both NGC 5194 (M51) and NGC 5457 (M101). There are multiple arms, but only two of the arms are bright. The faint secondary arms lie between the principal arms on the east side of the nucleus, completely filling the space between the bright arm closest to the nucleus on the north side and the extension of the second main arm in the northeast quadrant after it has spiraled through 360°. The illustration on the facing page was slightly overexposed to show these faint details. A negative reproduction is given in *Ap. J.*, *127*, 513, 1958, which shows not only the outer spiral features but also the details of the multiple dust lanes crossing the central lens.

Two principal dust lanes go into the very center of M100 in a spiral pattern. The center is illustrated on page *31*.

Most of the knots that appear in the two main spiral arms are H II regions, as can be seen from the reproduction of a plate sensitive to Hα and a second plate sensitive to an emission-free spectral region shown in figure 9 of the *Ap. J.* reference above.

Individual stars do appear in M100, but they are much fainter than the H II regions. Comparison of the illustration of M100 in the atlas with the negative prints in figure 9 of *Ap. J.*, *127*, is interesting. The photographic plate from which the negative print was made for the left half of the reproduction in *Ap. J.* is the same one that this atlas illustration comes from.

The estimated distance modulus of M100 is $m - M = 30.7$. Measurement on the original plate shows that, at this distance, the linear width of the two spiral arms averages about 900 parsecs—about 3 times the width of arms in M101 and about twice what is estimated for our own galaxy.

NGC 5236 is a magnificent southern spiral with multiple arms. The present illustration does not do justice to the intricate dust lanes or to the fainter spiral arms.

The galaxy has certain features common to an SBb, such as the straightness of the two dust lanes coming from the nucleus on opposite sides of a region of somewhat enhanced luminosity. On short-exposure plates, one lane appears to cut in front of the nucleus and the other goes behind. The pattern is similar to that of NGC 5383 on page *46*. There are two bright spiral arms and a number of arm fragments of lower surface brightness on the outside of the principal arms. The dust lanes that emerge from the nucleus follow the *inside* of the two bright arms. This is a general characteristic of most galaxies having opaque dust lanes. But dust is by no means concentrated in these two lanes; it is spread in spiral patterns over the entire face of the central lens. The segments are branched as in M51 and M101. The luminous spiral arms generally follow the branching of the dust lanes. Reproductions of M83 are also given by Shapley in his *Galaxies*, page 22, and as figure 2 of his *The Inner Metagalaxy*.

NGC 628   M74   Sc
PH–16–MH
Nov. 15/16, 1949
103aO
20 min
Enlarged 1.7×

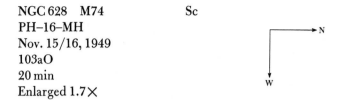

NGC 628 is of the M101 type of multiple-arm Sc but is more regular and symmetrical. The arms are not so highly branched, and the dust lanes are easier to trace. Again the dust lanes appear mostly on the inside of the luminous arms. Branching of luminous segments does occur from the two main arms which come from the nuclear region. These branches form the multiple-arm pattern. The distance modulus of NGC 628 is about 30.0. At this distance, the approximate width of the arms is 1000 parsecs.

NGC 1084   Sc
H–2354–H
Nov. 29/30, 1946
IIaO
10 min
Enlarged 7.1×

The three galaxies at the bottom of the facing page and the six on page *30* form a separate subgroup of Sc in which the spiral pattern is not so well defined as in the M101 type. The arms are usually not so "clean" and in some galaxies not so well separated from each other as those in the M101 group. The one main arm in the northwest quadrant of 1084 is well defined. It is lined on its inside edge with a dust lane. The spiral pattern on the east side of 1084 is not easy to trace as a single arm. Several dust lanes and segments of spiral arms are present. Notice the small nucleus of this galaxy.

NGC 4254   M99   Sc
PH–174–MH
Apr. 16/17, 1950
103aE
30 min
Enlarged 2.8×

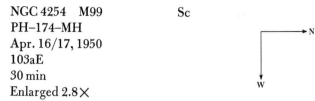

NGC 4254 is one of the bright spiral members of the Virgo Cluster. The distance modulus is about $m - M = 30.7$ for this cluster. At this distance, the spiral arms are about 1500 parsecs thick, which is considerably thicker than arms in M101 and thicker by a factor of 1.5 than arms in NGC 628. Dust lanes pervade the entire central lens. Most of the knots along the spiral arms are H II regions. Note the segments of spiral arms which break from the central regions in the northeast quadrant.

NGC 6181   Sc
H–2267–H
May 4/5, 1946
103aO
45 min
Enlarged 7.0×

Three well defined outer spiral arms are present in this galaxy: two on the east side, and one on the west side. The arms are thin. The distance modulus for 6181 is about $m - M = 32.4$. At this distance, the angular width of the arms corresponds to about 1200 parsecs. Notice the resolution of the arms into H II regions. The spiral pattern in the central regions is quite similar to that in NGC 157 (right).

NGC 4303   M61   Sc
PH–719–S
Apr. 6/7, 1954
103aO + GG13
30 min
Enlarged 2.2×

NGC 4303 is probably a member of the Virgo Cluster although it lies about 8° south of the main concentration. The redshift of 1557 km/sec makes it a likely candidate. The galaxy has some characteristics of a barred spiral. The central lens does not show well here but is like the lens in NGC 6951 (p. *46*). Two thin dust lanes (width about 150 parsecs) wind out through the pseudo bar to the inside of the beginning of the two main luminous arms. Many faint arms are present on the outside of the two bright ones. The many knots in the brighter arms are undoubtedly H II regions.

NGC 157   Sc
PH–1054–S
Aug. 24/25, 1955
103aO
30 min
Enlarged 9.4×

The first impression of this galaxy is that the entire surface is covered with luminous segments of spiral arms and interspersed dust lanes. One main dust lane is prominent on the inside of the arm that sweeps from the nucleus upward through the northeast quadrant. The amorphous nuclear region is very small, as in all nine galaxies of this special subgroup (NGC 1084, 6181, and 157 on this page and the six galaxies on the next page).

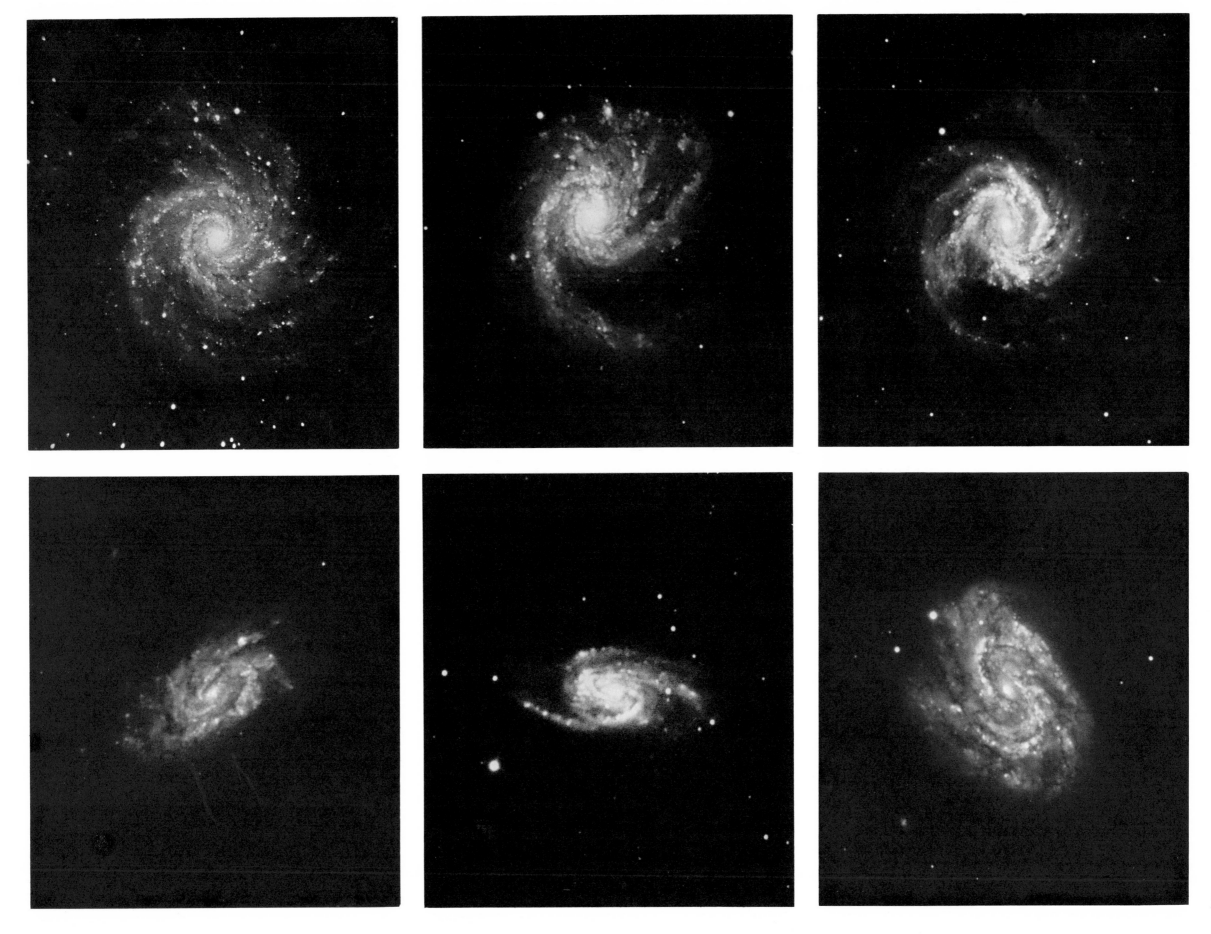

29

30

NGC 3810   Sc
H–15–S
Jan. 5/6, 1951
103aO
20 min
Enlarged 5.0✕

NGC 3810 and NGC 5962 (below) are the Sc counterparts to the "two-region-surface-brightness" galaxies like NGC 5055 and 1068 of the Sb section (pp. *15* and *16*). Spiral structure can be traced to within about *3* sec of arc radius (1 mm on the illustration) from the center. The distance modulus of 3810 is about $m - M = 30.4$. Three seconds of arc is 200 parsecs at this distance. The width of the outer arms is about 600 parsecs, which is somewhat smaller than the width in M101 or M51. The arms of 3810 are resolved into knots.

NGC 5962   Sc
H–2295–H
July 2/3, 1946
IIaO
30 min
Enlarged 7.0✕

NGC 5962 is similar to NGC 5055 (p. *15*) of the Sb systems. The central regions are of high surface brightness. Spiral structure is present in the inner regions and can be traced to within 0.7 mm (radius) from the nucleus on this illustration. The outer set of multiple arms are of low surface brightness.

NGC 1637   Sc
PH–68–MH
Feb. 15/16, 1950
103aO
30 min
Enlarged 3.6✕

The inner part of 1637, with a diameter of 22 mm on the illustration, is a completely symmetrical two-arm spiral. A second set of spiral arms, which dominate the east hemisphere, start as dust lanes between the nucleus and the main inner arm on the south side. These outer arms give the galaxy an asymmetry because there are no outer arms on the west side to match them. NGC 1637 is closer to us than the Virgo Cluster. The redshift gives a distance modulus of about 29.5. The arms of 1637 are resolved into stars and H II regions.

NGC 3672   Sc
H–2220–H
Jan. 6/7, 1946
103aO
60 min
Enlarged 5.0✕

NGC 3672 has multiple arms which begin from a very small nucleus. The nucleus is smaller than the seeing disk on the original negative, which was about 3 sec of arc. The arms are very thin and well defined in 3672. If the distance modulus is $m - M = 32.0$, the angular width of 3 sec of arc for the brightest arm sweeping through the northeast to the southeast quadrant corresponds to 370 parsecs. These are very narrow arms compared with the arms in most other galaxies. They do compare with the arms in NGC 488.

NGC 4088   SBc/Sc
S–1834–H
Jan. 17/18, 1939
Imp. Ecl.
60 min
Enlarged 7.1✕

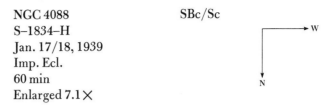

NGC 4088 has only two arms, which start at the end of a bar. This galaxy is closer to a pure SBc than to an Sc, but as it does have features which resemble NGC 157 (p. *29*) it is called a transition case. The bar and arms are of the (s) subtype, in which the arms spring from the ends of a bar rather than tangent to an internal ring. The distance of 4088 is probably 0.3 magnitude closer than the Virgo Cluster. Notice the resolution of the face of this galaxy into knots.

NGC 7314   Sc
PH–65–H
Oct. 13/14, 1950
103aO
30 min
Enlarged 3.0✕

The spiral pattern is dominated by dust lanes in NGC 7314. The arm segments on the west side are quite similar to the closely coiled arms in NGC 2841 (p. *14*). The nucleus of 7314 is very small. Spiral structure can be traced almost to its very center. The distance modulus of 7314 is about $m - M = 32.0$. The limit of the plate is about $m_{pg} = 23.0$. Consequently any resolved knots in the arms are brighter than $M_{pg} = -9.0$.

NGC 4321   M100   Sc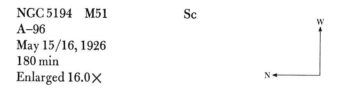
H–1602–H
Mar. 6/7, 1934
E40
15 min
Enlarged 25.0×

The four illustrations on the facing page are greatly enlarged reproductions of the nuclear regions of near-by Sc
galaxies. The spiral arms which begin near the center of
most galaxies are dust arms. The arms usually do not become luminous until they have left the nucleus. There is
no question that the dark regions between the luminous
arcs in this picture of M100 are filled with dust. Continuations of these dark lanes form the two principal dust
arms which wind out through the lens and end on the
insides of the two most luminous outer arms. Page *28*
gives the complete view of M100. The continuation of the
inner dust lanes shown here as they wind outward is best
shown in a negative print in *Ap. J.*, *127*, 513, 1958.

NGC 5457   M101   Sc
PH–185–MH
May 10/11, 1950
103aO
40 min
Enlarged 12.1×

The nucleus of M101 is similar to that of M100 (above).
Two principal dust lanes cut into the very center. It is
the dust rather than the luminous arcs that defines the
spiral pattern in this region. The two central dust patches,
however, unlike those in M100, cannot be traced as single
lanes into the outer regions. The entire inner lens of M101
is crossed by segments of dust arms. Although the segments, taken as a whole, define a spiral pattern, they cannot be connected with one another to form continuous
lanes.

The entire face of M101 is shown on page *27*.

NGC 5194   M51   Sc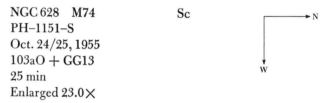
A–96
May 15/16, 1926
180 min
Enlarged 16.0×

The opaque dust lanes do not spiral into the nucleus as
in M100 or M101 but start tangent to a circular luminous
region centered on the nucleus. The central region is not
amorphous but is crossed by thin dust lanes in a hap-
hazard fashion. The two principal opaque lanes seen here
silhouetted against the edge of the bright center continue
to spiral outward. They eventually end up on the inside
of the two brightest spiral arms. See page *26*.

NGC 628   M74   Sc
PH–1151–S
Oct. 24/25, 1955
103aO + GG13
25 min
Enlarged 23.0×

The central dust lanes in NGC 628 are similar to those in
M51 (above). They begin tangent to the central lens and
do not go into the very nucleus. These two main lanes
wind outward on the inside of the principal luminous
spiral arms. The entire galaxy is shown on page *29*.

Plates taken in Hα light show many H II regions in the
arms. The largest of these regions is about 100 parsecs
in diameter, which is similar to the H II regions in M101
but smaller than the largest ones in either M33 or the
LMC.

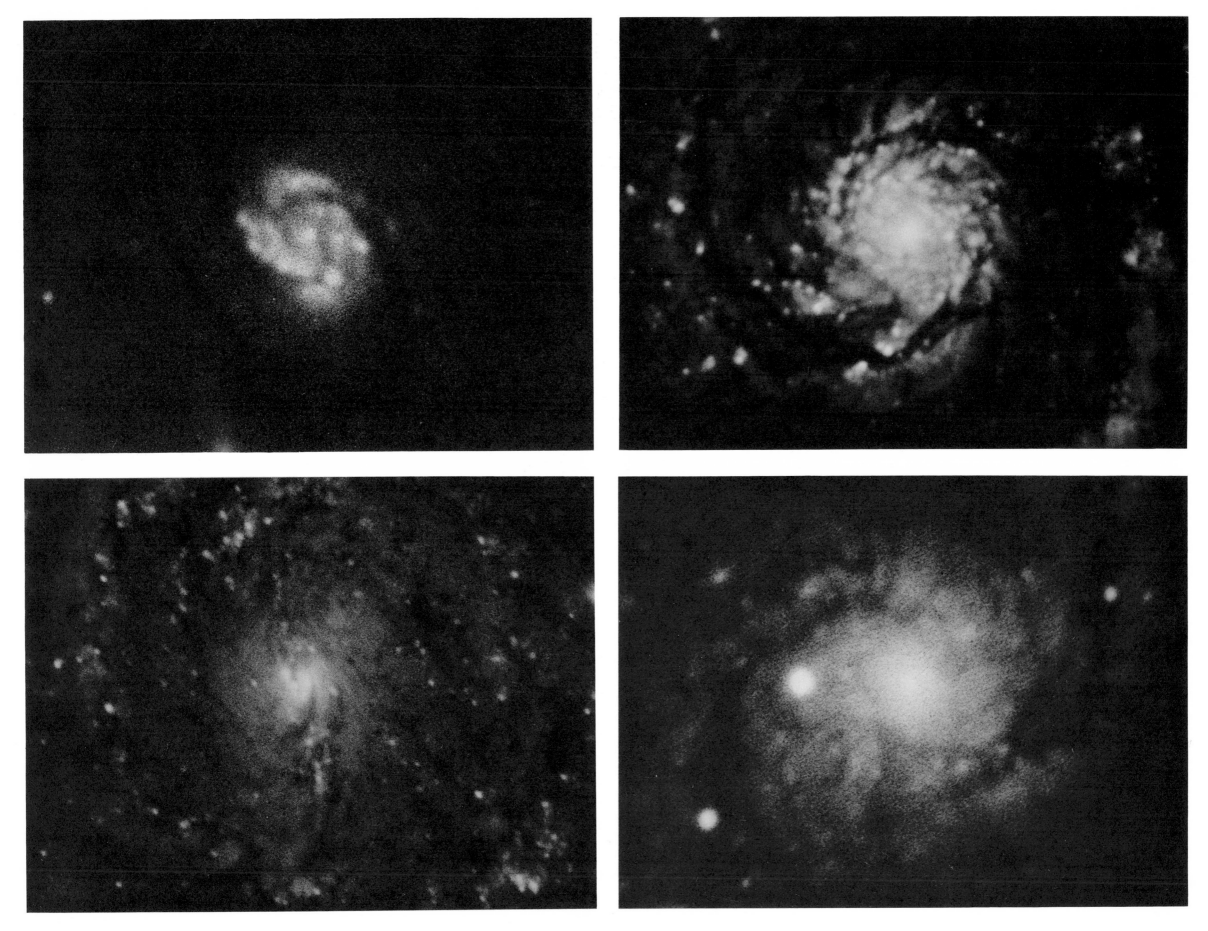

NGC 309   Sc
PH–15–MH
Nov. 15/16, 1949
103aO
20 min
Enlarged 6.0×

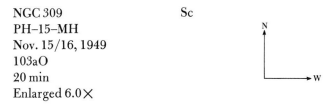

The spiral arms of all three galaxies illustrated on the facing page are of the multiple-arm M101 type. The feature that distinguishes all three galaxies is either the presence or the suggestion of an internal ring, tangent to which the spiral arms emerge. The arms in NGC 309 are narrow, well defined, and highly branched. The internal ring is almost complete. The spiral structure does not cross this ring and go into the nucleus. The nucleus itself is small (5 sec of arc in diameter) and amorphous.

Compare these three galaxies with the (r) subtypes in the Sb section (p. *21*) and in the SBb section (pp. *47* and *48*). The closest example of NGC 309 in the SBc section is NGC 1073 (p. *49*).

NGC 1232   Sc
PH–74–H
Oct. 14/15, 1950
103aO
30 min
Enlarged 2.0×

There is no complete internal ring in NGC 1232. However, the arms do not spiral out from the nucleus but rather begin tangent to the central amorphous nucleus and lens. Two principal arms originate on this central region. These arms branch into many segments soon after they leave the central lens. The branching of the arm which starts at the west point of the amorphous lens is particularly conspicuous. The arm branches almost immediately at this junction; each separate branch again divides after a turn of 120°. Additional divisions farther on form the multiple-arm pattern. The pattern resembles that of M101 but is slightly more regular.

NGC 5364   Sc
PH–193–MH
May 13/14, 1950
103aO
30 min
Enlarged 5.6×

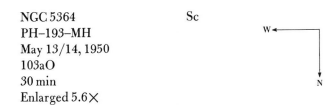

NGC 5364 is one of the most regular galaxies in the sky. The thin, bright, internal ring appears to be completely closed. There is spiral structure internal to this ring, but the inner arms starting from the nucleus are not well defined. The regular outer arms begin tangent to the bright ring. Two external arms are present. Their junction on the ring is difficult to find. The outer arm on the west side probably begins on the ring at nearly the west cardinal point. The beginning of the outer arm on the east side is near the north cardinal point. The outer west arm can be traced for about 450° from its origin on the ring. The outer east arm can be traced for 540° or one and a half revolutions from its origin. Dust lanes are not conspicuous over the face of this spiral, but faint lanes can be traced on the insides of the two main arms.

The redshift of NGC 5364 is 1357 km/sec (corrected for solar motion), which corresponds to a distance modulus of about $m - M = 31.3$. At this distance, the average angular width of the outer spiral arms corresponds to a linear width of 700 parsecs. This is larger by a factor of about 2 than the arms in NGC 488 and M101 but somewhat smaller than the arms in NGC 4254 (p. *29*), for example. The spacing *between* the center of the outer arms on the west side is about 3300 parsecs.

NGC 5248   Sc
PH–209–MH
May 15/16, 1950
103aO
30 min
Enlarged 5.0×

NGC 4258   Sb
PH–321–MH
Apr. 27/28, 1951
103aO
30 min
Enlarged 5.5×

This magnificent Sc galaxy shows a high degree of symmetry. The two principal inner spiral arms are of high surface brightness. Both arms contain conspicuous dust lanes on their inner edge. There is considerable dust silhouetted against the central lens. It forms multiple spiral lanes starting near the small nuclear region.

Five outer spiral arms of low surface brightness open wide from the central regions. They can be seen in the insert. The outer arms are branched. Two of the five hug the bright central region on the west side; they are stubby arms, of higher surface brightness than the remaining three. Two other of the outer arms start from the end of the bright inner arm at the northwest end of the major axis and can be traced for about 180° from the junction. The remaining outer arm begins at the southeast end of the major axis and spirals north through west. It is branched at its northwest end.

NGC 4258 is probably a member of the Ursa Major Cloud. The fact that the plane of this galaxy is inclined only 20° to the line of sight partly explains why the dust lanes are so prominent across the central lens of 4258. These lanes are quite chaotic. They do form a very rough spiral pattern throughout the central region. There are two principal luminous arms on the periphery of the bright central lens. Numerous knots, presumably H II regions, are present in these arms. Very faint spiral arms threading through the outer envelope can be seen in the insert. The outer arms are highly resolved into individual stars with the 200-inch. Normal novae have been found, but as yet no cepheid variables are known in 4258. A reproduction of 4258 in negative form, given by Hubble in *Ap. J.*, *97*, 225, 1943, shows the intricate detail of the dust pattern in the central region.

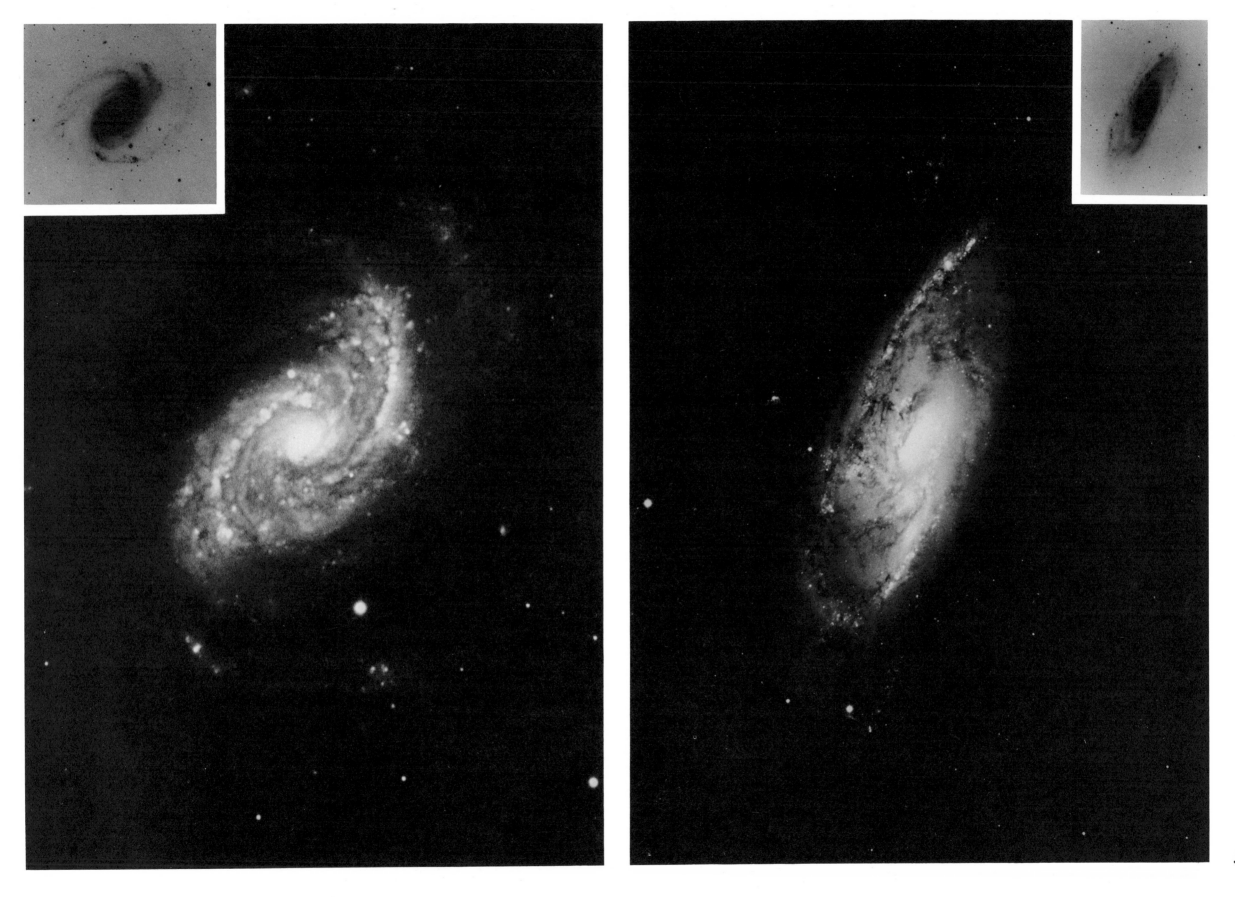

34

NGC 253   Sc
H–947–Δ
Sept. 2/3, 1945
103aO
50 min
Enlarged 3.0×

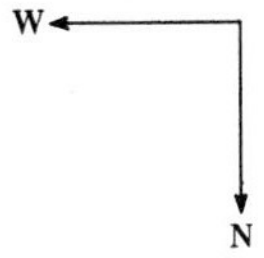

W ←——————┐
                  ↓
                  N

This spectacular spiral is the prototype example of a special subgroup of Sc systems. Other members of the group are shown on the next page. Photographic images of galaxies of the group are dominated by the dust pattern. Dust lanes and patches of great complexity are scattered throughout the surface. Spiral arms are often difficult to trace. The arms are defined as much by the dust as by the luminous matter.

Galaxies similar to the 253 class in the Sc can be identified in the Sa and Sb sections. Examples shown in the atlas are NGC 4293 of the Sa section (p. *11*) and perhaps NGC 972 and NGC 4433 of the Sb section (p. *23*).

The dust lanes in NGC 253 itself are conspicuous not only because a great deal of dust is present but also because the large angle of projection under which this galaxy is viewed provides for a radiation background against which the dust is seen. The fundamental plane of 253 is inclined only 12° to the line of sight.

The spiral arms in NGC 253 can be easily traced in this reproduction, but they are more easily seen in a negative print reproduced from the same original and shown by de Vaucouleurs in *Ap. J.*, *127*, 487, 1958, figure 8. The arms coming from the southwest end of the major axis are opening out of the page; the arms on the northeast end are going into the page.

The distance to NGC 253 cannot be found from the redshift because the galaxy is so close that any systematic redshift is concealed by the random motions. But the assumption that NGC 253 is like M31 both in linear dimensions and in absolute magnitude gives a distance of about 4×10^6 parsecs, which is about 5 times that of M31. The corresponding distance modulus is $m - M = 28.0$. These values may be uncertain by a factor of 2.

NGC 2903   Sc
PH–71–MH
Feb. 15/16, 1950
103aO
30 min
Enlarged 1.3×

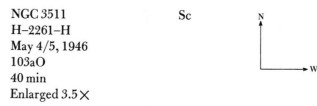

The internal pattern of dust is almost as intricate in NGC 2903 as it is in NGC 253. The galaxy is seen more nearly face on, and is more distant than 253, so that the delicate dust filaments threading across luminous regions are lost in 2903, but there is no question that these patterns are present. The nucleus is composed of about eight intense knots, presumed to be giant H II regions. The reproduction is overexposed in the central regions and does not do justice to the intricate pattern. Two thin, regular spiral arms are present in the outer regions of 2903.

NGC 6643   Sc
S–985–Δ
Aug. 3/4, 1948
103aO
40 min
Enlarged 8.1×

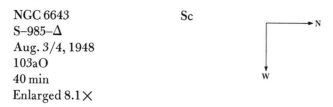

The spiral pattern is easier to trace in 6643 than in 253. The arms are visible on this plate, owing primarily to the knots (probably H II regions) present over the face of the system. The central nucleus is exceedingly tiny here. The spiral arms are multiple. The internal dust pattern resembles that in 2903 and 253.

NGC 3556   Sc
S–1742–H
Dec. 6/7, 1937
Imp. Ecl.
60 min
Enlarged 4.0×

NGC 3556 is a member of the 253 class. It is seen almost on edge. A negative print, made from the same original, is shown by de Vaucouleurs in *Ap. J.*, *127*, 487, 1958.

Note the lack of a central nuclear bulge. If a large nuclear region were present it would be visible in this photograph because the galaxy is nearly on edge. Compare this illustration with the Sc systems on page *25*.

NGC 4793   Sc
H–2273–H
May 5/6, 1946
103aO
40 min
Enlarged 8.3×

Many condensations are present over the face of NGC 4793. These, together with a small nucleus and internal dust, put NGC 4793 in the 253 class. The condensations are probably H II regions.

NGC 3511   Sc
H–2261–H
May 4/5, 1946
103aO
40 min
Enlarged 3.5×

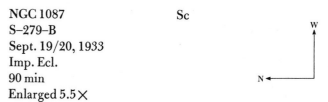

The pattern of NGC 253 and 3556 is repeated in this galaxy. Notice the very small nucleus and the ill-defined spiral arms.

NGC 1087   Sc
S–279–B
Sept. 19/20, 1933
Imp. Ecl.
90 min
Enlarged 5.5×

NGC 1087 has an extremely small nucleus. There is a multiple spiral structure defined more by the dust lanes than by luminous matter.

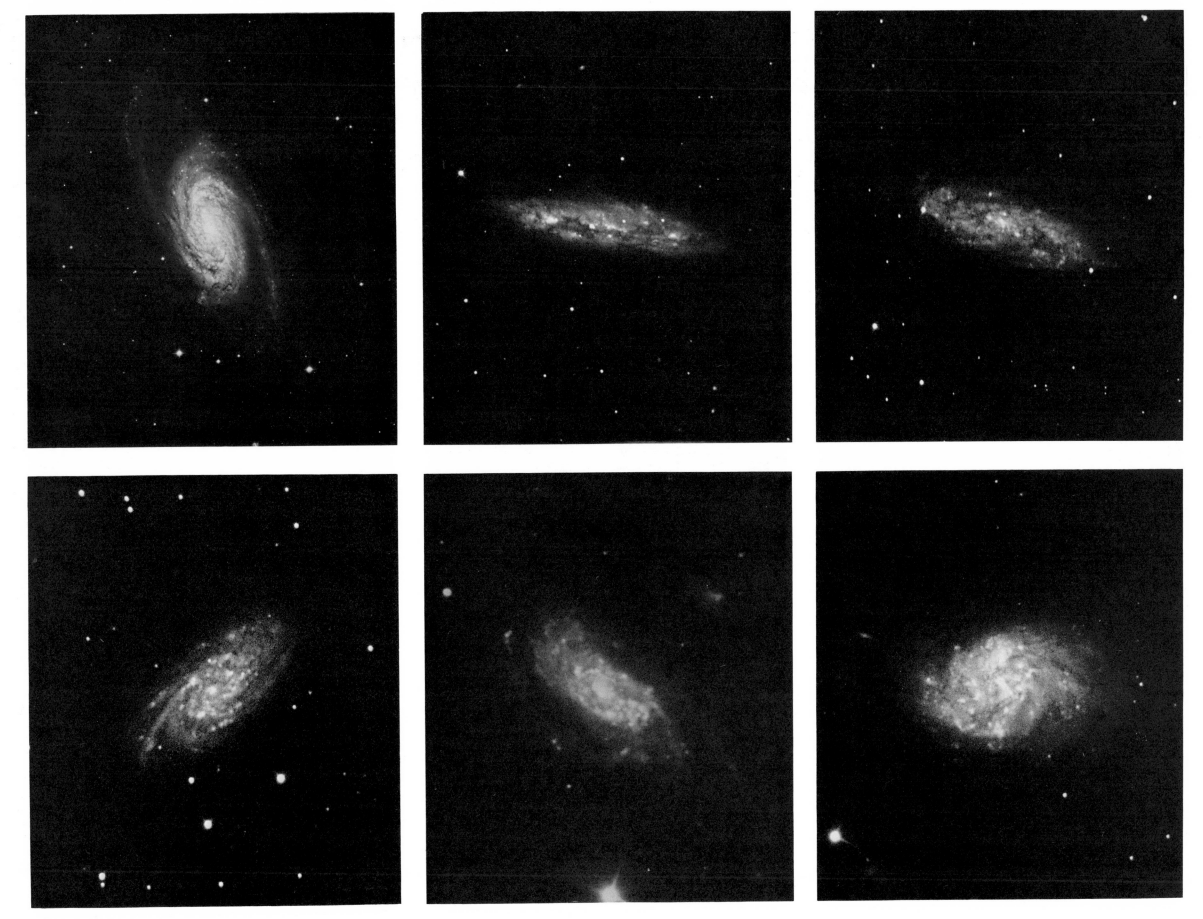

36

NGC 598   M33   Sc
PS–421   N
Jan. 6/7, 1951
103aO
12 min   W
Enlarged 4.9×

NGC 2403   Sc
PH–344–B   N
Nov. 6/7, 1950
103aO + GG1
30 min   W
Enlarged 2.0×

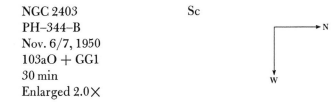

NGC 598 (M33) is the nearest Sc to our own galaxy. It is a member of the Local Group. The distance modulus is probably close to $m - M = 24.5$ (Sandage, *Ap. J.*, *127*, 513, 1958). The limiting magnitude of the 200-inch is about $m_{pg} = 23.0$. This means that the stellar content of M33 can be studied in detail down to stars of absolute magnitude $M_{pg} = -1.5$. Bright O and B stars, cepheid variables, globular and open star clusters, novae, irregular variables, and H II regions are known in M33. The first extensive study of the stellar content was made by Hubble in 1926 (*Ap. J.*, *63*, 236, 1926). No comparable study has been made in recent times.

Spiral structure is easy to trace in M33. The arms are "massive" in the sense used by Reynolds and by Hubble (*Observatory*, *50*, 1927). The arms are completely resolved into bright stars. Most of these are blue supergiants, but there are also at least 3000 red supergiants of $M_V = -5$ which are similar to those found in h and χ Persei.

The brightest H II region is NGC 604, in the northeast quadrant. This has a linear diameter of about 320 parsecs. Many smaller H II regions abound in the spiral arms. Detailed, large-scale photographs of parts of M33 are given as negative prints in *Ap. J.*, *127*, 513, 1958.

The integrated color index of the system is CI (International) = 0.40 (Holmberg).

NGC 2403 is similar in form and in stellar content to M33. It is a member of the M81 group. The distance modulus is about $m - M = 27.1$ (*A. J.*, *59*, 180, 1954). This is the first galaxy beyond the Local Group in which cepheid variable stars were found with the 200-inch. Twenty-seven variables have been isolated so far (1960). Ten of them are definitely cepheids with periods ranging from 18 to 54 days. Many of the others are undoubtedly cepheids, but periods are not yet available. No novae have been found in NGC 2403. The comparison of the number of novae found in M81 (Sb) and in NGC 2403 (Sc) shows that the same disparity exists as between M31 and M33, and probably indicates that novae are very infrequent in Sc galaxies as compared with Sb.

Over 100 H II regions, many of them irregular in shape, are known in 2403. The largest of the regions measures 20 sec of arc in diameter, which corresponds to 270 parsecs at the assumed distance. This diameter is a bit smaller than that of NGC 604 in M33 and considerably smaller (by a factor of 2.3) than 30 Doradus in the LMC. NGC 2403 and other members of the M81 group are important for the calibration of the extragalactic distance scale.

NGC 925   Sc/SBc
PH–71–S
Dec. 26/27, 1951
103aO + WG2
15 min
Enlarged 2.5×

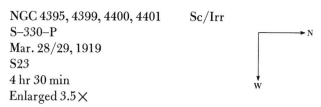

The four galaxies shown on the facing page are very late Sc. Some authors, including Shapley, have called galaxies of this type Sd. All four systems have rather low surface brightness, have spiral arms which are sometimes difficult to trace, and are highly resolved into stars and H II regions. NGC 925 is a member of a group of galaxies with NGC 1023, 891, 1058, 1003, and IC 239 as members. The mean redshift of this group is about 500 km/sec. The distance modulus corresponding to this redshift is $m - M = 29.0$. There are many H II regions in the arms of 925, the largest of which has an angular diameter of about 5 sec of arc, corresponding to 170 parsecs at the assumed distance.

NGC 45   Sc
PH–116–H
Sept. 24/25, 1951
103aO
25 min
Enlarged 2.0×

NGC 45 has one of the lowest surface brightnesses of any galaxy in the sky. This reproduction has been double-printed from the original 200-inch negative to increase the contrast. The entire face of NGC 45 is covered with resolved stars. There must be very little internal absorption due to dust because many background galaxies can be seen through the main body of NGC 45. This galaxy is a member of a group of near-by systems of large angular diameter which includes NGC 24, 45, 55, 247, 300, and 7793. This is probably the nearest group of galaxies to the Local Group, but it is too far south for adequate work from the northern hemisphere.

NGC 4395, 4399, 4400, 4401   Sc/Irr
S–330–P
Mar. 28/29, 1919
S23
4 hr 30 min
Enlarged 3.5×

This galaxy is so loose and disconnected that visual observers counted each of four of the brighter patches as individual nebulae and catalogued them as separate objects in the New General Catalogue. The surface brightness is so low, and the plate so underexposed, that this reproduction has been double-printed; i.e., a copy negative was made from the original plate, and the print on photographic paper was made from the copy negative. This process increases the contrast. Note the extreme resolution into stars. Spiral arms can be traced, but the general pattern resembles that of the Large Magellanic Cloud.

NGC 5204   Sc/Irr
PH–1170–S
Dec. 14/15, 1955
103aO
25 min
Enlarged 6.2×

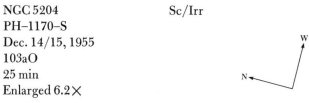

Notice that the entire face of NGC 5204 is resolved into stars. It is difficult to trace any spiral pattern in this system. This is a transition case between a very late Sc and an Irr system of the Magellanic Cloud type. NGC 5204 is a member of the M101 group and therefore must have about the same modulus as M101 itself, which is estimated to be $m - M = 27.0$. The limiting magnitude of this plate is about $m_{pg} = 22.5$. Therefore, all resolved stars visible in this illustration are brighter than $M_{pg} = -4.5$. E. Holmberg has studied the integrated properties of NGC 5204, and his paper should be consulted for details (*Medd. Lunds Astr. Obs.*, ser. II, no. 117).

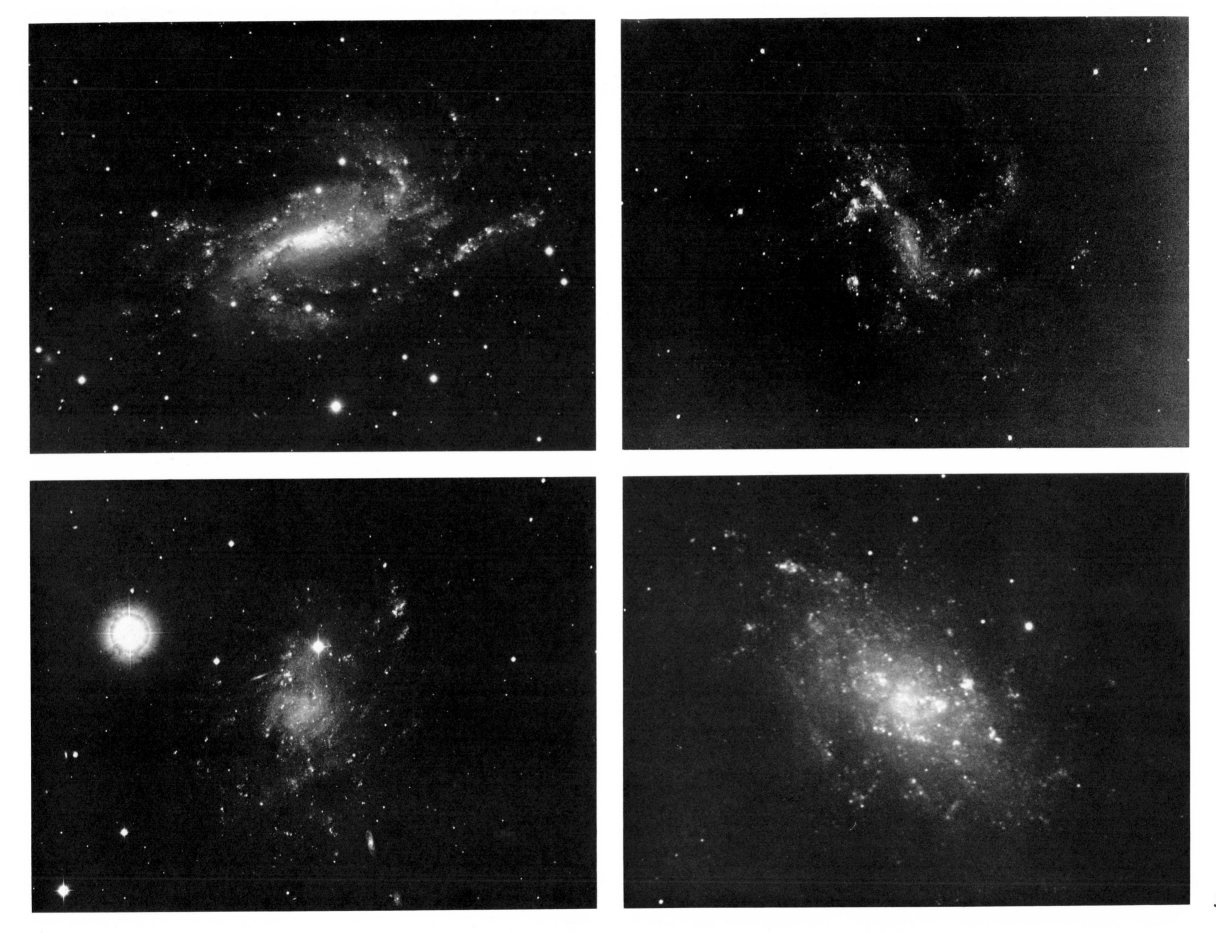

LMC   Irr I
BEX-164
Nov. 4/5, 1951
103aE + Red plexiglass
Enlarged 1.6×

This is the Large Magellanic Cloud. The plate was taken
by Dr. Karl Henize with the Mount Wilson 10-inch refractor in the light of Hα. Although the form of this galaxy suggests the lack of rotational symmetry, it is known
from the 21-cm radiation of neutral hydrogen [Kerr, Hind-
man, and Robinson, interpreted by Kerr and de Vaucouleurs (*Aust. J. Phys.*, *8*, 508, 1956)] that the LMC is
rotating. De Vaucouleurs believes that the LMC has a
flattened equatorial plane inclined at 65° ± 5° to the line
of sight (*A. J.*, *60*, 126, 1955). He also believes that a
very faint spiral pattern can be traced over the face of the
cloud, but the degree of spiral structure is certainly of a
different order from that in galaxies classed as Sa, Sb, and
Sc. The idea that this and the Small Magellanic Cloud
may be highly flattened systems is interesting because it
suggests that irregular galaxies are not so disorganized as
first inspection of photographs indicates.

The LMC contains many H II regions, open star clusters, globular star clusters, and cepheid variable stars. It
and the Small Cloud are the most important single galaxies in the sky, because they are the systems where the
tie-in of the absolute magnitudes of cepheids with normal
stars must be made. The distance modulus for both
clouds is about $m - M = 19.2$. They are 10 times closer
to us than M31.

A catalogue of the H II regions in the LMC is given by
Henize in *Ap. J. Supp.* Sec., *II*, no. 22, 315, 1956. A summary discussion of the stellar content is given by Bus-
combe, Gascoigne, and de Vaucouleurs in the *Supplement
to the Australian Journal of Science*, *17*, no. 3, 1954.

The largest H II region in the LMC is 30 Doradus. It
is a complex region containing overlapping Strömgren
spheres. Henize gives the dimensions of the nebulosity
as 1849 sec by 1781 sec of arc. At a distance modulus of
$m - M = 19.2$, these angles correspond to 640 parsecs by
615 parsecs. These dimensions are of the same order (a
factor of 2 larger) as those of NGC 604 but are much larger
than the Orion Nebula and other large Hα complexes that
have so far been recognized in our own galaxy.

NGC 1156   Irr I
PH–1078–S
Aug. 25/26, 1955
103aO
30 min
Enlarged 4.1×

This galaxy is highly resolved into stars and H II regions. Slight suggestions of a chaotic spiral structure might be made, but the pattern, if present, is very weak.

NGC 2366   Irr I
PH–555–B
Oct. 31/Nov. 1, 1951
103aO + GG1
30 min
Enlarged 2.2×

This is a member of the M81 group. Note the two separate parts to this galaxy. Several bright H II regions are visible, the two most conspicuous being located together at the southwest end of the larger part. The smaller satellite segment also contains H II regions. All stars resolved in 2366 are brighter than $M_{pg} \approx -4.1$. Most of the resolved stars are blue.

NGC 3109   Irr I
S–524–B
Mar. 6/7, 1937
Imp. Ecl.
100 min
Enlarged 4.1×

This galaxy may be a greatly flattened system seen nearly on edge. No spectroscopic measurements for rotation have been published. The face of the galaxy is resolved completely into stars, H II regions, and stellar associations. This reproduction is from a copy negative because the original plate could not be found. There is considerable plate grain caused by the recopying process.

IC 2574   Irr I
PH–706–S
Feb. 28/Mar. 1, 1954
103aO + WG2
30 min
Enlarged 1.6×

This galaxy, sometimes called Coddington's nebula, is a member of the M81 group. Note how most of the H II regions are concentrated at the north end of the "bar." The brightest resolved stars also occur in this region. This giant association is about 1500 parsecs along the major axis (which is almost in the east-west direction). All stars resolved in this reproduction are brighter than $M_{pg} = -4.1$.

Ho II   Irr I
PH–48–S
Nov. 29/30, 1951
103aO + WG2
30 min
Enlarged 2.0×

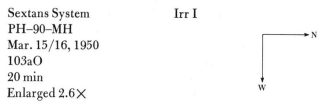

This is one of the members of the M81 group. It was discovered by E. Holmberg during his study of the M81 group (*Medd. Lund Obs.*, ser. II, 128, 1950). Its membership in the M81 group was proved by N. U. Mayall's redshift determination (*A. J.*, *61*, 97, 1956). The distance modulus of the M81 group is about $m - M = 27.1$. The limiting magnitude of the plate from which this reproduction is taken is about $m_{pg} \approx 23.0$. Hence all resolved stars shown over the face of Ho II are brighter than $M_{pg} \approx -4.1$. There are many H II regions in Ho II.

Sextans System   Irr I
PH–90–MH
Mar. 15/16, 1950
103aO
20 min
Enlarged 2.6×

The Sextans System is probably an outlying member of the Local Group (see Humason and Wahlquist, *A. J.*, *60*, 254, 1955). The distance modulus is probably 25.0. Note the almost rectangular pattern of the resolved stars. The diameter of the concentration of bright stars near the last corner of the pattern is about 200 parsecs.

40

IC 1613   Irr I
PS–624
Oct. 18/19, 1952
103aO
10 min
Enlarged 6.0×

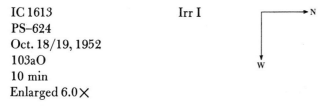

This is a well known member of the Local Group. Many cepheid variables have been discovered by Baade in IC 1613. The distance modulus is about 24.0. Note the concentration of the brightest stars into one corner of the galaxy. This grouping into large associations is a common feature of Irr galaxies of the Magellanic Cloud type.

NGC 4449   Irr I
H–520–H
Jan. 21/22, 1925
E40
105 min
Enlarged 4.0×

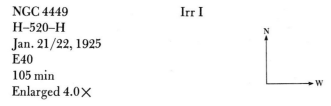

There are many H II regions in this galaxy, concentrated mostly in the northern part where many knots appear in this illustration. Dust patches are scattered through the central regions. One is particularly well shown on the eastern boundary of the galaxy.

NGC 4214   Irr I
PH–913–S
Mar. 26/27, 1955
103aO + WG2
30 min
Enlarged 1.5×

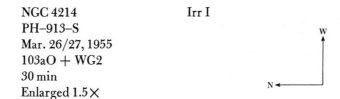

This galaxy is highly resolved over its entire face into individual stars and H II regions. This reproduction is from a plate taken under poor seeing conditions. Furthermore, the nuclear region is not well shown in the print because of overexposure. The original plate shows complete resolution to the center. A supernova was discovered in this galaxy in 1954 by P. Wild (Harvard Announcement Card 1250).

NGC 4656/7   Irr I
S–457–H
Mar. 18/19, 1925
E40
110 min
Enlarged 4.0×

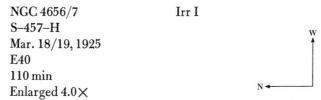

This peculiar irregular is very asymmetric in its surface brightness. The galaxy on one side of the nucleus is bright; on the opposite side, it is very faint. There are two segments on the faint side. The galaxy is well resolved into stars and H II regions.

Dwarf, 1023 Gr., No. I   Irr I/Sc
PH–337–S
Jan. 18/19, 1953
103aO + WG2
20 min
Enlarged 4.0×

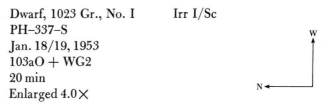

This galaxy and the one below were found during inspection of 48-inch Schmidt plates of the NGC 1023 group of galaxies (see Humason et al., *A. J.*, *61*, 97, 1956, table XI). Eight galaxies of the type of these two systems were found in the area of the NGC 1023 group, all of very low surface brightness. The distance modulus of the NGC 1023 group is probably near $m - M = 29.3$ (mean redshift $= 513$ km/sec; $H = 75$ km/sec 10^6 parsecs). The plate limit of $m_{pg} = 23.0$ means that the individual resolved knots are brighter than $M_{pg} = -6.3$.

Dwarf, 1023 Gr., No. III   Irr I/Sc
PH–308–S
Jan. 8/9, 1953
103aO + WG2
30 min
Enlarged 4.1×

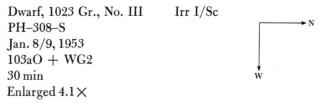

It is probable that most of the eight are dwarf members of the 1023 group, because a search of a similar area of the sky on adjacent Schmidt plates failed to show any objects of this type. These two reproductions were made from copy negatives; i.e., the original plates have been copied and then printed to increase the contrast.

    There may be some suggestion of spiral structure in both 1023, Dwarf I, and 1023, Dwarf III, but it is certainly not well marked. Consequently these two dwarf galaxies are classified with the Irregulars.

NGC 3034   M82   Irr II
PH–51–S
Nov. 29/30, 1951
103aO + WG2
30 min
Enlarged 3.0×

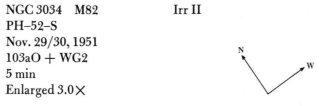

M82 is the prototype of the irregular galaxies of the second type. Note the extremely filamentary wisps at the boundary of the galaxy. There is no suggestion of resolution into stars or knots, although the distance of M82 is about the same as that of M81 (p. *19*).

NGC 3034   M82   Irr II
PH–52–S
Nov. 29/30, 1951
103aO + WG2
5 min
Enlarged 3.0×

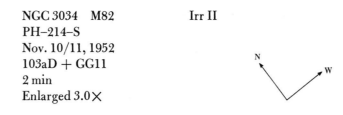

There is much dust across the face of M82. This illustration and the one below are from short-exposure plates. The integrated properties of M82 seem contradictory. The color index of the system as a whole is CI=0.86 (Stebbins and Whitford, *Ap. J.*, *115*, 284, 1952). This color, plus the amorphous texture of the luminous regions, suggests a stellar content like that of elliptical galaxies or the center of Sb galaxies. But the integrated spectral type of M82 is A5 (Humason, *A. J.*, *61*, 97, 1956). These features are not understood at present.

NGC 3034   M82   Irr II
PH–214–S
Nov. 10/11, 1952
103aD + GG11
2 min
Enlarged 3.0×

NGC 520   Irr II
PH–176–H
Sept. 3/4, 1953
103aD + GG11
40 min
Enlarged 4.0×

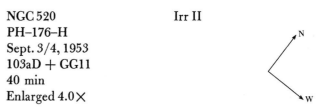

NGC 520 has the smooth texture of M82 and has a prominent absorption patch crossing the face. Thin extensions, of low surface brightness, are visible in this illustration. Inspection of the original plate suggests that NGC 520 is not a collision of two galaxies but rather a system of the M82 type.

NGC 3077   Irr II
PH–896–S
Jan. 23/24, 1955
103aD + GG11
30 min
Enlarged 4.0×

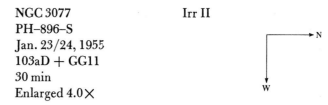

This is a member of the M81 dynamical group. The texture of the luminous regions and of the absorption patches silhouetted against them is similar to that of M82. Another galaxy with this same pattern is NGC 5195 (the companion to M51 shown on p. *26*). Probably NGC 4691 (shown on p. *44*) is also of this type.

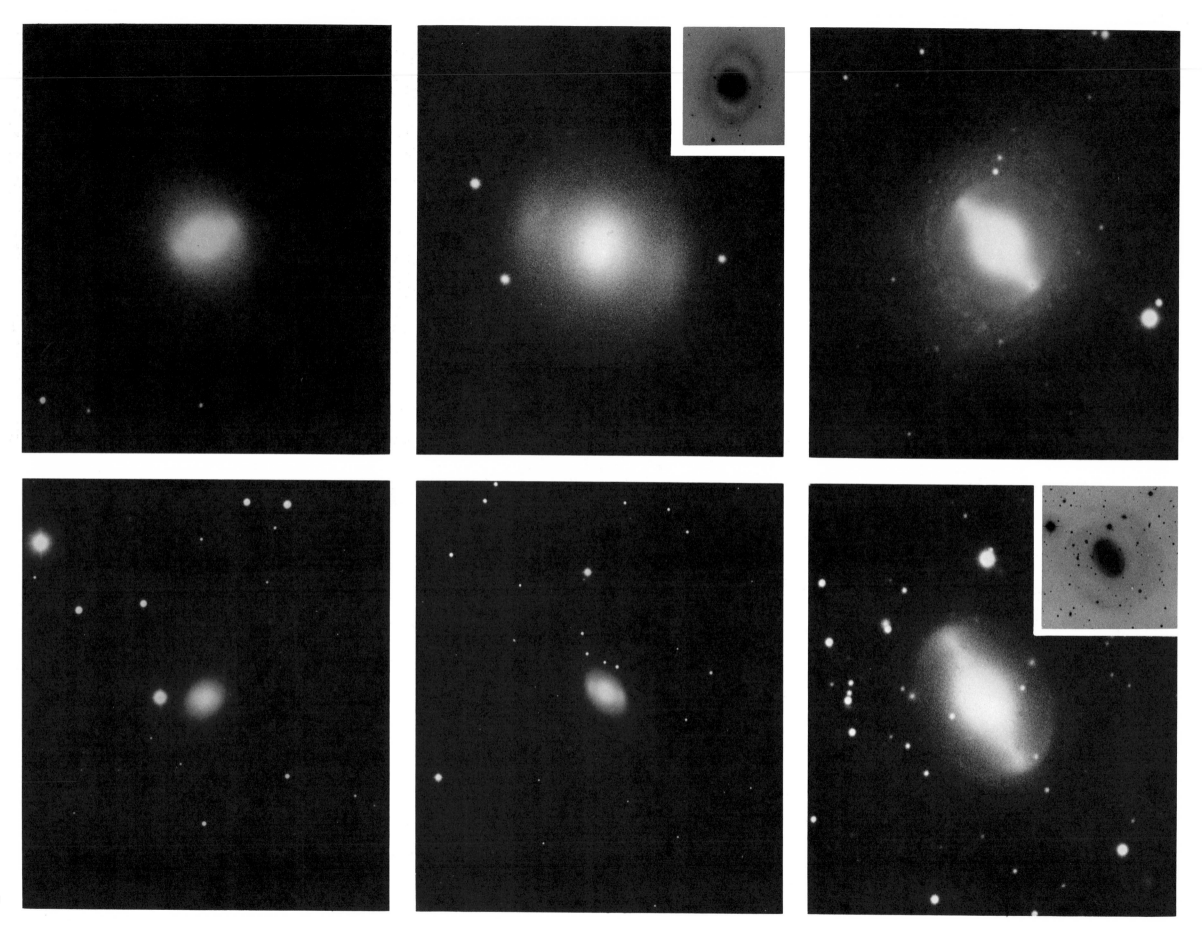

NGC 4262   SB0$_{2/3}$
PH–905–S
Mar. 24/25, 1955
103aD + GG11
45 min
Enlarged 7.1×

N ↑ W →

The bar has bright ansae which terminate inside the apparent boundary of the lens. The ansae are not completely separate from the rest of the bar, as in NGC 2859 (right). Because of this, the galaxy is a transition case between an SB0$_2$ and SB0$_3$ type.

NGC 4612   SB0$_1$
PH–687–S
Feb. 9/10, 1954
103aO + WG2
30 min
Enlarged 2.2×

N ↑ W →

This is a particularly good example of an SB0$_1$ galaxy, but the features of the bar are so tenuous that very little shows in the illustration. The pencil drawing below shows the major features. The axis of the bar is inclined about 15° to the minor axis of the lens and of the external ring. This ring is extremely faint and does not show at all in the photograph; its position relative to four of the stars can be found from the diagram.

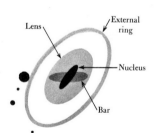

NGC 2859   SB0$_2$
PH–852–S
Nov. 2/3, 1954
103aO
30 min
Enlarged 7.1×

W ↑ N ←

This is the type example of the SB0$_2$. The bar is fuzzy and indistinct. There is a brightening of the rim of the lens at two opposite ends. There are no sharp boundaries anywhere. The bar makes an angle of 15° to the minor axis of the envelope and of the outer ring. The external ring appears to be completely detached and unbroken. Its boundaries are very indistinct, but the inner edge is sharper than the outer.

NGC 2950   SB0$_{1/2}$
PH–665–S
Feb. 5/6, 1954
103aO + WG2
30 min
Enlarged 2.2×

W ↑ N ←

The nucleus, the lens, and the brightening of the rim of the lens are all similar to those features in NGC 2859 (above). The bar is inclined about 30° to the minor axis of the lens. Since the bar is nearly as thick as the nucleus, the galaxy is called a transition between SB0$_1$ and SB0$_2$. There is either a broken external ring or very indistinct nearly circular spiral arms. The pencil drawing shows the major features.

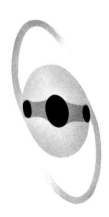

NGC 4643   SB0$_3$/SBa(r)
PH–688–S
Feb. 9/10, 1955
103aO + WG2
30 min
Enlarged 3.5×

N → W ↓

The nucleus, lens, bar, and inner envelope of this galaxy are of the SB0$_3$ type. There is very faint but definite spiral structure outside the inner envelope, however. There appears to be a circular dust ring which makes a complete revolution touching the ends of the bar. The thin spiral pattern outside the dust ring winds outward through a tenuous outer envelope. A few knots in the spiral arms show the beginning of resolution into what are probably H II regions.

NGC 5101   SB0$_3$/SBa(s)
PH–906–S
Mar. 24/25, 1955
103aD + GG11
45 min
Enlarged 4.5×

W ↑ N ←

The inside lens is "broken" at both ends of the bar. A very faint arm structure begins at the ends of the bar. This pattern is not circular as in NGC 2859 but is broken into a rudimentary spiral pattern shown in the insert. This galaxy would be called SB0$_3$ on poor or small-scale plates, but this reproduction from a 200-inch plate indicates an exceedingly early SBa(s).

NGC 2217   SBa(r)
H–2028–H
Oct. 21/22, 1938
Agfa Blue
80 min
Enlarged 4.2×

Note the well developed bar (of the SB0₃ type) which ends on the rim of the tenuous lens. The arms begin at diametrically opposite points on the rim of the lens about 15° counterclockwise from the termination of the bar. These arm connections are of extremely low surface brightness and are difficult to trace. The connections are nearly tangent to the lens, move straight for about 10 mm (on the illustration), and then turn sharply through 90° and begin the nearly circular arm pattern, which looks at first glance like a complete ring.

NGC 2217   SBa(r)
H–2028–H
Oct. 21/22, 1938
Agfa Blue
80 min
Enlarged 4.2×

The arms *do not* form a complete ring but lap over each other near their junction after each arm has spiraled through 180°. The pattern is similar to that of the arms in NGC 3185 but is more difficult to trace because of projection effects.

NGC 7743   SBa(s)

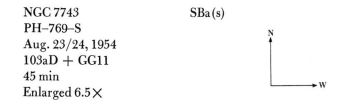

PH–769–S
Aug. 23/24, 1954
103aD + GG11
45 min
Enlarged 6.5×

The arms are of very soft and smooth texture. This is the SBa prototype of the (s) subgroup. It resembles NGC 1300 of the SBb(s) sequence. There is no suggestion of dust lanes or absorption patches across the face of this galaxy. On the 200-inch plate there is a hint of a very low-surface-brightness outer elliptical ring concentric with the nucleus with a semimajor diameter of 2 min (65 mm on the illustration).

NGC 5566   SBa(r)
PH–908–S
Mar. 24/25, 1955
103aD + GG11
45 min
Enlarged 3.0×

This is the only good example of an SBa(r) galaxy shown in the atlas. The reproduction is overprinted for the nuclear regions, to bring out the faint arm pattern and the two thin dust lanes. The insert shows the complete internal ring with the broad, rather ill-defined bar that terminates on the ring. Note that the bar is not along the major axis of the projected ring.

NGC 175   SBa(s)

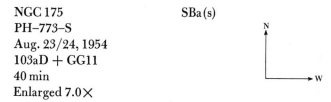

PH–773–S
Aug. 23/24, 1954
103aD + GG11
40 min
Enlarged 7.0×

This galaxy is a very late SBa(s). The arms are tightly wound and form a nearly complete ring as in NGC 3185 (below) and NGC 2217 (left). The arms show limited resolution into knots. They tend to branch into soft filaments which are not tightly wound.

The bar is well developed and of the SB0₃ type.

NGC 3185   SBa(s)

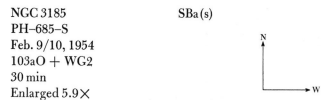

PH–685–S
Feb. 9/10, 1954
103aO + WG2
30 min
Enlarged 5.9×

At first glance this galaxy appears to have a complete external ring. The bar seems to terminate on the ring, but close inspection shows that the "ring" is composed of two closely coiled spiral arms. Each arm can be traced from its starting place at the end of the bar, through 180°, until it passes near and almost joins the opposite end of the bar. Each arm passes beyond the opposite end of the bar and can be traced on the outside of the beginning of the other arm. This closely coiled spiral pattern of nearly overlapping arms is repeated in other galaxies such as NGC 2217 (left) and NGC 3081 (Sa, p. *11*).

A very faint external elliptical ring or possibly spiral arm system is visible on the original plate. It has a semimajor diameter of about 70 sec of arc, which is about 35 mm on the scale of the illustration. It is difficult to trace, but the major axis of the ring appears to have the same orientation as the major axis of the arm system.

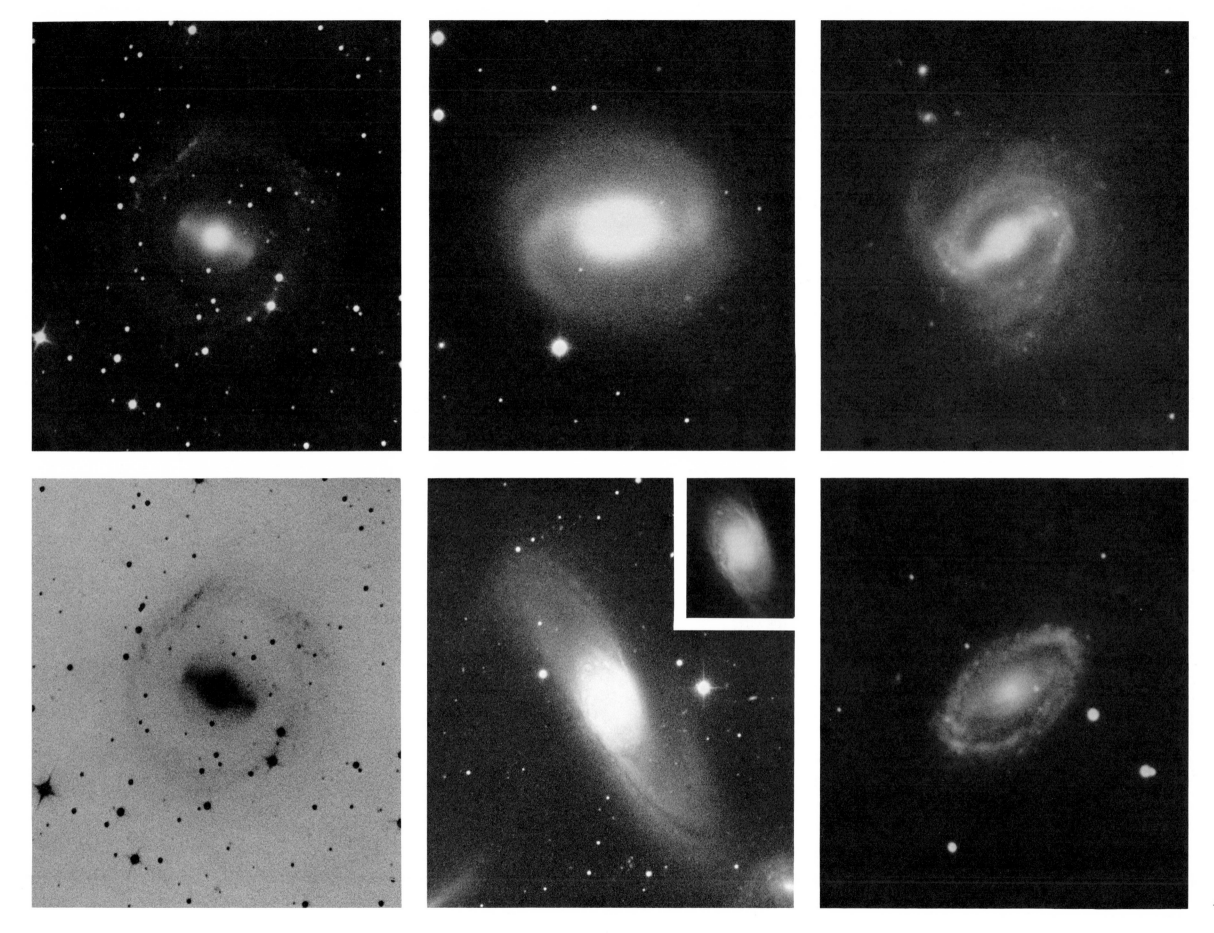

43

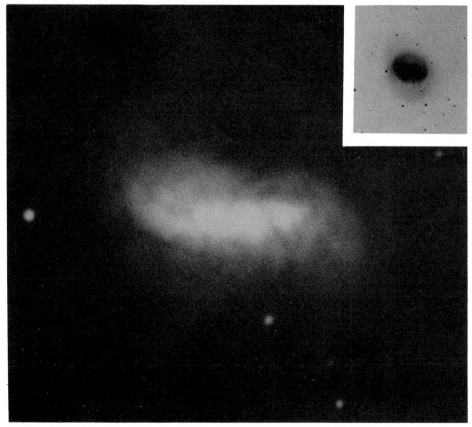

44

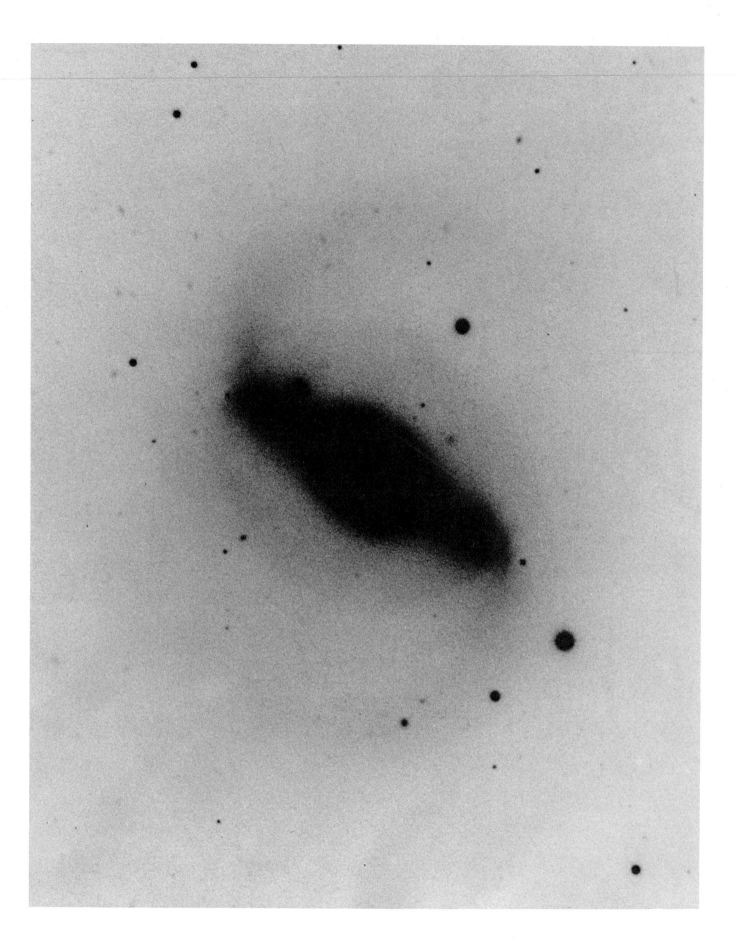

NGC 4314   SBa(s)pec
H–2041–H
Nov. 27/28, 1938
Imp. Ecl.
80 min
Enlarged 10.0×

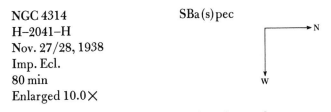

This galaxy is peculiar because of the internal structure
in the bar. The complete spiral pattern at the center of
the bar is not connected in any way with the external arms
seen in the negative reproduction on the right. The bar
itself is of smooth texture. A few dust patches are superimposed upon the bar. The direction of opening of the
two internal spiral arms is the same as that of the very
faint external arms shown on the right.

NGC 4314   SBa(s)pec
PH–192–MH
May 13/14, 1950
103aO
30 min
Enlarged 8.0×

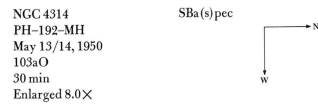

The smooth external arms of low surface brightness and
the prominent amorphous bar place this galaxy in the SBa
class. Note the elliptical lens. The bar terminates on the
edge of the lens. The two thin, almost circular spiral arms
spring from the ends of the bar. They can be traced for
only about 130° before their surface brightness becomes
so low that they are lost in the night sky background.

NGC 4691   SBa pec (Hubble)
PH–928–S   Irr (M82 type) (Sandage)
Mar. 28/29, 1955
103aO + WG2
30 min
Enlarged 9.1×

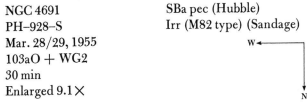

Hubble classified this galaxy as an SBa pec because, on
short-exposure plates, the external structures (shown in
the insert) looked like spiral arms and the central structure looked like a bona fide bar of a barred spiral. It was
evident that the bar had much internal obscuration. This
200-inch plate shows that the external structures are really not arms but complete arcs of luminous matter.

NGC 1300   SBb(s)   N
PH–75–H   ↑
Oct. 14/15, 1950 |
103aO |___→ W
30 min
Enlarged 7.5✕

NGC 1300 is the prototype of the pure SBb(s). The bar is
distinct and smooth in texture. Two straight dust lanes
emerging on opposite sides of the nucleus can be traced
to the ends of the bar, where they turn sharply and follow
the insides of the spiral arms. The arms form nearly complete ellipses. The foci of each ellipse are the nucleus and
the end of the bar of the opposite arm. Each arm can be
traced through about 340°.

NGC 5383   SBb(s)
No. 195 (60″)
Apr. 3/4, 1913
3 hr
Enlarged 14.6×

Note the two nearly straight dust lanes threading into the bright central region. The lane coming from the lower left appears to cross in front of the nucleus; that coming from the upper right passes behind the nucleus.

NGC 3504   SBb(s)/Sb
PH–1169–S
Dec. 14/15, 1955
103aO
30 min
Enlarged 5.9×

The dust lanes are not well shown in this illustration. The lane starting from the nucleus in the upper left is quite straight, as in all normal SBb(s). The lower right lane is slightly curved into a spiral pattern. The dust lanes spiral into the nucleus similarly to those in M100 (p. *31*) and NGC 1097 (top right). NGC 3504 is a transition type between SBb and Sb.

NGC 1097   SBb(s)
H–2025–H
Oct. 21/22, 1938
Agfa Blue + GG1
90 min
Enlarged 3.1×

There is a reproduction of NGC 1097 in *Observatory*, *78*, 125, 1958, by J. L. Sérsic, which shows the complex nuclear structure. The two straight dust lanes, seen on the face of the broad bar, spiral toward a central point as they reach the bright, overexposed part of the reproduction. This is similar to the pattern near the center of M100 (p. *31*) and resembles somewhat that of NGC 4314 (p. *44*).

NGC 6951   SBb(s)/Sb
PH–113–H
Sept. 24/25, 1951
103aO
30 min
Enlarged 5.0×

This galaxy, which has features of both SBb(s) and Sb systems, is a transition between these two "pure" spiral types. The two straight dust lanes are prominent. In form this galaxy is similar to NGC 1097 (above).

NGC 1398   SBb(r)
PH–178–S
Oct. 25/26, 1952
103aO + WG2
30 min
Enlarged 4.0✕

NGC 4394   SBb(sr)
PH–425–MH
Apr. 16/17, 1952
103aO
30 min
Enlarged 6.2✕

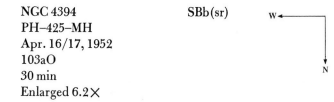

This is the type example of the SBb(r). Note how the spiral arms start tangent to an external "ring." The ring is not complete but is composed of nearly circular spiral segments. The faint external arms are difficult to trace as continuous bands. They tend to break into segments. Neglecting the slight discontinuities, the two principal arms can be traced for about one and a quarter revolutions from their origin on the internal "ring."

    There are no straight absorption lanes in the bar, as is characteristic of the NGC 1300 type of SBb.

NGC 4394 is intermediate between the NGC 1300 type SBb(s) and the NGC 1398 type SBb(r). The arms spring from the ends of the bar as in NGC 1300, but they spiral rather tightly, just missing the other arm after spiraling 180°. This feature is similar to the spiral structure in 3185 SBa (p. *43*) and 2217 SBa (p. *43*). There are no straight absorption lanes in the bar as in the 1300 type.

47

48

NGC 2523   SBb(r)

PH–850–S

Nov. 2/3, 1954

103aO

30 min

Enlarged 6.0×

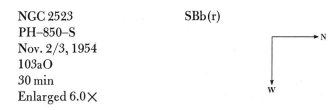

The four illustrations on the facing page show the progressive development of the ringed form along the SBb(r) section. NGC 2523 is the earliest of the four. Note the thin arms and the nearly complete circular ring. The major axis of the ring and of the spiral pattern is inclined about 60° to the junction of the bar with the ring. In general, barred spirals seen in projection have a random orientation of the position angle of the bar with the major axis of the ring.

NGC 3351   M95   SBb(rs)

PH–315–S

Jan. 8/9, 1953

103aD + GG14

30 min

Enlarged 3.0×

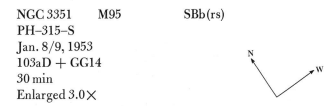

This is the broken-ring type similar to 3185 SBa (p. *43*) or 2217 SBa (p. *43*). The nearly circular arms forming the broken ring spring from the ends of the bar and wind slightly outward, almost touching the opposite bar and arm after a revolution of about 180°.

The nuclear region of 3351 has an almost circular ring which shows on the original plate but is lost in the reproduction. This ring is broken at two points, from which dust lanes emerge. This region is somewhat like the center of 4314 (p. *44*) and 1097 (p. *46*).

NGC 4593   SBb(rs)

PH–929–S

Mar. 28/29, 1955

103aO + WG2

30 min

Enlarged 4.0×

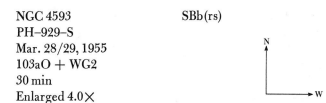

The internal circular ring is nearly complete but it is of nonuniform brightness around the periphery. One spiral arm begins at the end of the bar. The other begins about 110° around the ring (counted counterclockwise) and can be traced for nearly one and a quarter turns.

NGC 4548   SBb(sr)

PH–914–S

103aO + WG2

Mar. 26/27, 1955

30 min

Enlarged 3.6×

The internal ring is not complete. The arms do not begin at the ends of the bar as in NGC 1300 type systems but start tangent to the amorphous central region about 90° from the termination of each end of the bar. The characteristic absorption features are present in the bar but are not so regular as in NGC 1300.

NGC 3367   SBc(sr)
H–2268–H
May 4/5, 1946
103aO
30 min
Enlarged 8.1×

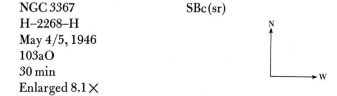

This is basically of the 1300 type, but the arms almost coalesce to form an internal ring. The arm starting at the northeast end of the bar winds through about 200° and then branches. The arm coming from the southwest end of the bar is not well defined at its beginning. It branches for the first time after about a 90° turn. Other branching takes place after about 340°. The arm can be traced through a turn of about 400°.

NGC 7741   SBc(s)
PH–66–H
Oct. 13/14, 1950
103aO
30 min
Enlarged 4.1×

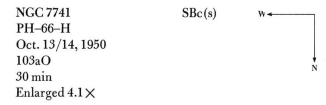

The bar is resolved almost completely into knots. There are dust patches in the bar but no straight lanes as in the NGC 1300 type of SBb. Note the dust lanes on the inside of the spiral arms.

NGC 1073   SBc(sr)
PH–82–H
Nov. 11/12, 1950
103aO
30 min
Enlarged 2.5×

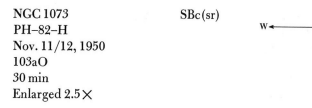

The arms do not begin from the ends of the bar but rather about 30° from the bar's termination. There is no complete circular ring. The arms and the bar are resolved into many knots. There are no straight absorption lanes in the bar.

NGC 2525   SBc(s)
H–2477–H
Jan. 9/10, 1948
103aO
30 min
Enlarged 6.5×

This and NGC 7741 are the SBc prototypes of the (s) subgroup. This galaxy is an early SBc. The bar, though not resolved into knots, is not as smooth textured as the bar in NGC 1300; the nucleus at the center is small and has a high surface brightness. The arms are resolved into knots.

NGC 3359   SBc(rs)
PH–55–H
Apr. 27/28, 1949
103aO
30 min
Enlarged 3.0×

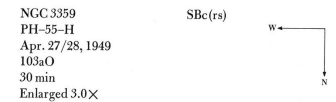

This is of the broken-ring type. There is a high degree of resolution of both the bar and the arms into knots. This galaxy was illustrated by Hubble in his article showing the first pictures from the 200-inch, *Pubs. A. S. P.*, *61*, 121, 1949.

NGC 7640   SBc(s)
PH–115–H
Sept. 24/25, 1951
103aO
30 min
Enlarged 1.2×

This galaxy is nearly on edge, but there is little doubt that it is an SBc of the (s) subgroup. The two spiral arms make a sharp angle at the ends of the bar, one arm sweeping behind the bar, the other sweeping nearly in front of it. The arms are resolved into stars.

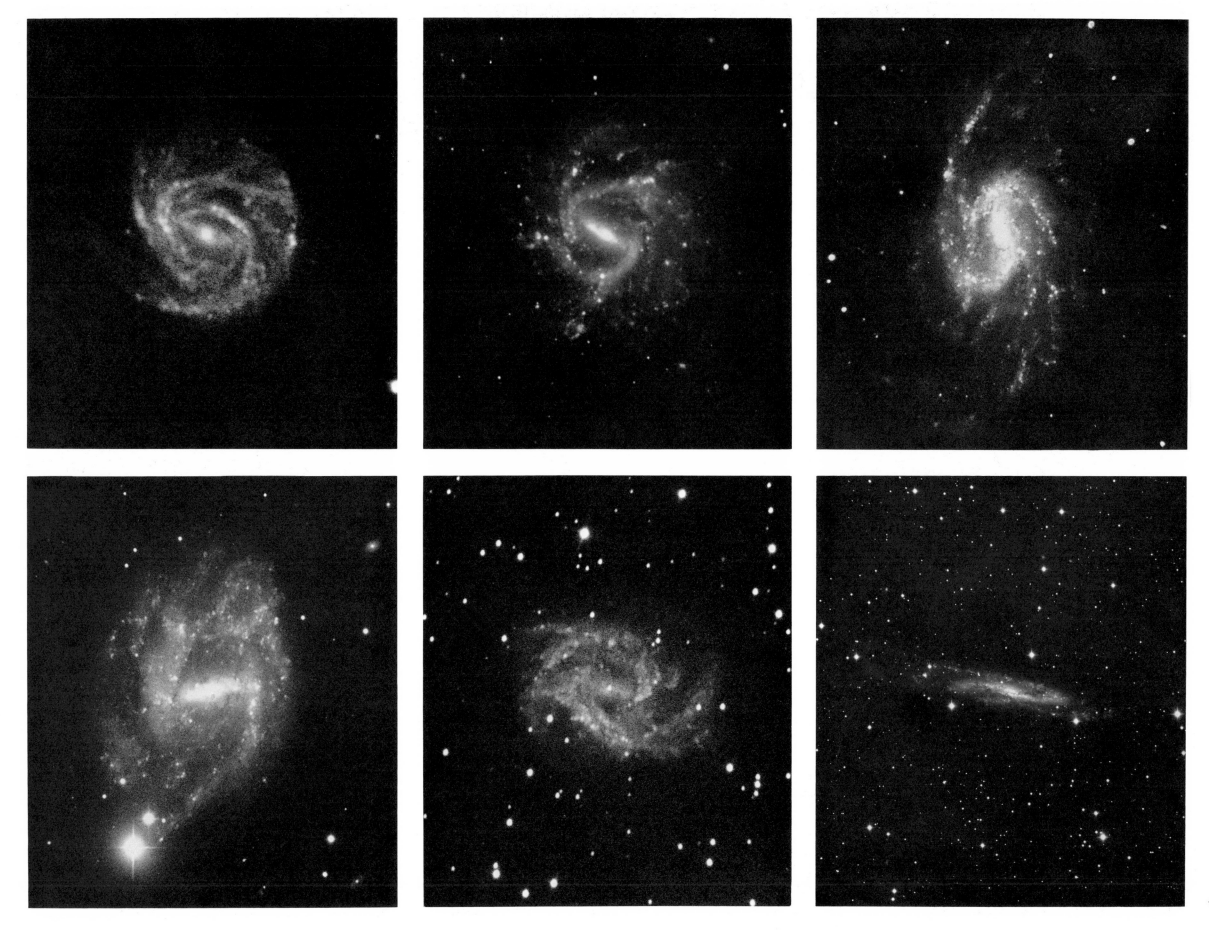

49

NGC 5128   (E0 + Sb)?
PH–161–Mi
May 23/24, 1952
103aD + CG3486
40 min
Enlarged 3.5×

W ←

N

NGC 5128 is one of the most peculiar objects in the sky. The background resembles that of an E0 galaxy, but the wide and highly opaque absorption lane across the center is unique. The lane is much wider and more chaotic than lanes in Sb and Sc galaxies seen on edge. For this aspect, compare 5128 with NGC 4594 (p. *24*) or any of the galaxies on page *25*.

NGC 5128 is a source of intense radio emission. Observations by Mills show that the strongest emission originates in the absorption band. Baade and Minkowski have published negative prints of NGC 5128 which illustrate both the position of the strong radio source and the features of the dust lane. Bolton, Westfold, Stanley, and Slee (*Aust. J. Phys.*, 7, 96, 1954) found that, in addition to the strong radio radiation of the dust lane, a weaker radiation comes from a nearly circular area 2° in diameter centered on 5128. This area is larger than that in which the optical radiation has yet been traced. The most recent summary of the radio work on NGC 5128 is given by C. A. Shain in the volume of the Paris Symposium on Radio Astronomy, 1958.

Baade and Minkowski believe that NGC 5128 is two galaxies in collision. The geometry of the situation is not completely clear. Several points in the illustration help in the interpretation. The background luminosity of that part of the image on the northwest side of the absorption lane is smooth, with no dust patches superposed. The surface on the opposite side of the dust lane is covered with a patchy pattern of obscuration. This pattern could be reproduced if the dust were in a thin plane of an Sb or Sc galaxy like NGC 253 (p. *34*), for example. If this plane were tipped about 20° to the line of sight with the rotational axis coming out of the paper, the observer would see part of this plane superposed on the background of the E0 galaxy but only on the upper half. The lower half

of the E0 galaxy would be completely free of the image of the Sb and would therefore show no absorption patches. If the background E0 galaxy were removed we might expect to see an image somewhat like that of NGC 7331 (p. *17*) or possibly NGC 4216 (p. *25*) at a slightly greater angle. The absorption lane across 5128 is very wide and does not resemble that in 7331. There may be two reasons for this. The first is a geometrical one, the second dynamical. (1) If we really see a dusty Sb or Sc superposed on an E0, the dust lanes are not expected to look like those of a normal galaxy such as 7331 because there is an intense background radiation field (the E0) upon which the dust of the Sb or Sc can be silhouetted. Any dust present will be much more conspicuous than normally. (2) If an actual collision is taking place, some of the kinetic energy of the center of mass of the galaxies may be transferred to the contents of the galaxies, in particular to the gas and dust. If part of the energy is pumped into the dust layer, this layer will become more distended against the gravitational potential due to the galaxy as a whole and the lane will appear to be wider and more disorganized than in normal Sb or Sc systems.

J. L. Sérsic has obtained isophotal contours of NGC 5128. He describes the appearance of the image and gives absorption data in *Observatory*, 78, 24, 1958. He states that "the central region of the band (dark lane), which is more conspicuous in the red light, presents a complex structure formed of chains of condensations — probably chains of high-luminosity O-B stars — separated by lanes of obscuring matter." He assigns an apparent magnitude to the stars in the chains as $m_{pg} = 18.7$. There is no evidence whatsoever on PH–161–Mi for chains of stars in the bright region of the central dust lane. Rather, the texture of the luminosity is smooth. Dust lanes are interspersed, but the luminous matter is not broken into knots or condensations.